OIL

IN THE SOVIET UNION

HISTORY · GEOGRAPHY · PROBLEMS

OIL
IN THE SOVIET
UNION

HISTORY · GEOGRAPHY · PROBLEMS

BY HEINRICH HASSMANN

Translated from the German
with the addition of much new information
By ALFRED M. LEESTON

Foreword by E. DeGolyer

PRINCETON, NEW JERSEY

PRINCETON UNIVERSITY PRESS

1953

This book was originally published
by Industrieverlag von Hernhaussen K.G., Hamburg,
under the title
Erdöl in der Sowjetunion: Geschichte, Gebiete, Probleme

Printed in the United States of America
by Princeton University Press at Princeton, New Jersey

FOREWORD

As the free world faces Russia and her satellites behind the Iron Curtain, it is highly desirable that we know what her capacity to produce petroleum and its products may be. Petroleum products are a war munition of decisive importance and one which accounted for more than half of our overseas shipments during the last war. As the *New York Times* has remarked editorially, it is not the infantry but gasoline which is now queen of battles.

The secrecy regarding petroleum resources which was maintained by the Soviets until the past year was of recent origin. For the Seventeenth International Geological Congress which met in Russia during 1937, they published a series of excellent guide books in English, and foreign geologists and technologists were invited to attend—and many did attend—excursions through the oil fields, including those of the Second Baku, the great Permian basin lying east of the Ural Mountains. By the time we became their ally, the Iron Curtain had begun to close. Our country lend-leased or gave the Soviets several refineries. They were unwilling to reveal even the locations where these refineries were to be erected and seemed more anxious to secure a number of small plants of different processes than to secure plants which could be most quickly constructed and would be of greatest utility. Fundamentally they were more interested in our technology than in the very material assistance which was being given.

Production figures were not published by the Soviets during the war, nor were they published from the suspension of hostilities until recently. Occasional claims of increased production have been made but not expressed volumetrically. Generally, they have been stated in percentages of the goals of some Five-Year Plan, details for which were not available. The Soviet Minister for the Oil Industry reported on the state of the industry to the Party Congress held in Moscow, October 1952. The veil of secrecy has been lifted to some degree. Production figures are now available. Claims are made of the discovery of new oil regions of undisclosed location.

Dr. Leeston's translation of Dr. Hassmann's work is presented as the best general survey of the Russian oil economy presently available. It doubtless contains many errors. Any study of the inadequate data accessible to us almost certainly would be faulty. Consideration

[v]

of figures released by the Soviets since the initial publication of this book, however, indicates that the Hassmann estimates are good.

Geography favors our free world. The oil reserves of the Middle East are not nearly so available to the Soviet Union as Dr. Hassmann implies in his epilogue. If by some circumstance they should come under the control of the Soviet Union they would be even more vulnerable to military attack than is the Baku region, the present chief source of Soviet supply. The vulnerability of the Baku region was clearly recognized by the late Joseph Stalin and stated by him to our former ambassador to Moscow, General Walter Bedell Smith. The Middle East is even more vulnerable. Furthermore, the great current production of the Middle East comes from relatively few wells, wells which could be denied easily. The nature of Soviet aggression being what it is, it also requires the reduction at least to satellite status of the nations within whose boundaries the oil reserves are found and thus involves their loss of sovereignty. Clearly the strategy of the Soviet Union calls for the building-up of a less vulnerable source of supply in the interior of Russia, and to this end the Soviets appear to be concentrating their efforts.

E. DE GOLYER

Dallas, 1953

TRANSLATOR'S PREFACE

THE favorable response of expert critics to the original German edition of Dr. Hassmann's *Erdöl in der Sowjetunion* prompted the translation of his book. It seemed desirable to make available to the American reader this survey of the Soviet oil industry, because it discusses numerous aspects of importance today and contains information not readily available elsewhere.

The translator wants to add that, except in clearly marked translator's additions, the opinions expressed in this book are entirely the author's and do not necessarily represent those of the translator.

No changes have been made in the text or the author's figures, although all measurements but tons (which are always *metric* tons) have been converted to standard American units. However, to bring the book up to date and enhance its usefulness, the translator has added a number of footnotes, maps, a translator's appendix giving the most recent data, a brief bibliography and an index.

ALFRED M. LEESTON

Dallas, 1953

AUTHOR'S PREFACE

UNTIL recently so many countries tried to make their decisions independently of, and without relation to, those of other sovereign states that neither a uniform trend in world politics nor a common denominator for world events was recognizable. However, nations now have but one political election: the East-West alternative; the choice between cooperation with the United States of America or the Soviet Union, two nations representing distinctive but strongly antagonistic ways of life.

This world-wide controversy is reflected in many ways in political, cultural, military, and economic fields. Inextricably involved in this clash of two divergent ideologies is petroleum, which occupies a key position in our highly mechanized age. However, while the United States has a good supply of oil in rich reserves at home and in foreign concessions located largely around the Caribbean Sea and the Persian Gulf, and controlled by major oil companies, the petroleum supply of the Soviet Union is very questionable. This fact lends credence to the assumption that Soviet domestic and foreign policies (for instance, in the Middle East, where one of the richest oil regions in the world is located, on the doorstep of the Soviet Union) are influenced by the Russian domestic problem of securing a sufficient oil supply. This study, therefore, is not to be limited to a consideration of economic factors, but will deal with the whole scope of the Russian oil situation, extending far beyond the narrow framework of economics alone. Only against a background of world politics and economics can the peculiarity and significance of the Russian oil industry be viewed adequately.

However, a study with such comprehensive aims meets with considerable difficulty on account of the lack of information on events in the vast Russian Empire, and also from mutual prejudice and distrust. Complete, systematic reports of the Russian petroleum industry are lacking in all phases of the work. The few monographs extant are limited to special problems. This absence of reliable literature is understandable in view of the difficulty of obtaining the necessary data. The Soviet Union discontinued publication of official statistics as such in 1938. Instead, production figures are published as percentages of the total production scheduled in the Five-Year Plans. This makes evaluation very difficult. Comparison of such percentage statistics with production figures of former years or of other countries is quite complicated.

This realistic report on Soviet petroleum is made possible only by a very careful collection of available figures, interpretation of the few domestic and foreign publications, and the use of official Soviet information by the author.

Critical sifting and appraisal of the available material make clear the risk of unfair decisions in view of increasing international tension, even in situations where political and economic factors should take precedence over personal convictions and tenets. The Iron Curtain concept that divides our world into two hostile camps is so strongly entrenched in our consciousness that East and West cannot listen to each other without prejudice. In the face of this atmosphere of skepticism and mutual distrust, the author desires by all means to emphasize that the present treatise attempts to keep aloof from such a tendency. This essay takes into account the existing political situation and, in particular, the economic system of the Soviet Union, but has nothing to do with the military aspect or ideological bias. Rather, the author has set himself the aim of presenting objectively the basic condition of the Russian petroleum industry: its development, current situation, and problems.

HEINRICH HASSMANN

Hamburg, 1951

CONTENTS

Foreword   v

Translator's Preface   vii

Author's Preface   ix

PART I. THE BASIS OF THE RUSSIAN OIL INDUSTRY   1

The Russian economic region   3

Territory. Population. History. Constitution. Economy.

The Russian economic system   10

Soviet economic theory. Economic provisions of the Soviet constitution. Various periods of the Soviet economy. Soviet economic achievements.

PART II. THE DEVELOPMENT OF THE RUSSIAN OIL INDUSTRY   19

The development of the czarist oil industry   21

The czarist empire and the oil industry. Oil areas and oil production in czarist times. Oil companies and their investments in the czarist era. Oil processing and domestic demand in the czarist era. Transportation problems and oil exports in the czarist era. The end of the czarist oil industry.

The development of the Soviet oil industry   33

State authority and the oil industry. Oil geology and geophysics. Drilling and production techniques. Oil production and refining. Oil exports and domestic consumption. The pattern of the Soviet oil industry.

PART III. THE REGIONS OF THE SOVIET OIL INDUSTRY   63

The southwestern regions   67

Baku. Groznyy. Maykop. Georgia. Dagestan. The Turkmen area. The Central Ukraine. The Western Ukraine. Oil shale in Estonia.

CONTENTS

The eastern regions   84

The Molotov oil region. The Ufa oil region. The Kuybyshev oil region. The Saratov natural-gas area. The Emba region. The Ukhta-Pechora area. The Central Asiatic oil area. Sakhalin Island.

PART IV. PROBLEMS OF THE RUSSIAN OIL INDUSTRY   107

The oil demand of the Soviet Union   109

Can the oil demand of the Soviet Union be compared with the oil demands of other countries? What factors determine the Russian oil demand? Can the Soviet oil demand be curtailed without injury to the economy?

The satisfaction of the oil demand of the Soviet Union   122

Is Russian oil production encouraged or hampered by the Soviet economic system? Does the Soviet Union have the oil reserves and the personnel to increase production? Is the steel supply of the Russian oil industry assured? Can synthetic-oil production make a substantial contribution to the Russian oil supply? How much of the Russian oil demand can be covered by imports?

EPILOGUE. THE SOVIET UNION AND THE MIDDLE EAST   139

Author's Appendix   145

Translator's Appendix, Bibliography, and Index   153

MAPS AND CHARTS

Fig. 1. Vegetation zones of the European USSR   4

Fig. 2. Vegetation zones of the Asiatic USSR   5

Fig. 3. Europe: sedimentary basins, oil and gas fields, pipelines, refining centers, and oil-handling ports   36-37

Fig. 4. The USSR: oil-field development and principal transport facilities   48

Fig. 5. The Baku area   68

Fig. 6. The Northern Caucasus: Georgia, Dagestan, the Maykop area, and the Groznyy area   71

Fig. 7. The Turkmen Soviet Socialist Republic   76

Fig. 8. The Ukrainian Soviet Socialist Republic   78-79

Fig. 9. The Baltic region, including Estonia   83

Fig. 10. The Central Urals, including the Molotov area   88

Fig. 11. The Urals, including the Ufa and Molotov areas   90

Fig. 12. The Middle Volga region, including the Kuybyshev area   92

Fig. 13. The Lower Volga region, including the Saratov area   93

Fig. 14. The western half of the Kazakh Soviet Socialist Republic, including the Emba region   96

Fig. 15. The European North, including the Ukhta-Pechora area   98

Fig. 16. The Fergana Valley   100

Fig. 17. The Uzbek Soviet Socialist Republic   101

Fig. 18. Sakhalin Island   104

Fig. 19. Oil production in the world, the U.S.A., and Russia   113

TABLES

1. Survey of Soviet production   18
2. Russian oil production from 1908 to 1916   25
3. Production of the oil companies of Russia from 1910 to 1914   27
4. Foreign investment in the Russian oil industry in 1914   28
5. Distribution of British capital among Russian oil regions   28
6. Survey of finished products made in Russian refineries in 1910   30
7. Comparison of Russian oil exports with oil production   31
8. Comparison of domestic consumption with exports of Russian oil products (annual averages for the years 1910-1913)   32
9. Geological prospecting of Russian territory   39
10. Number of geophysical crews used in exploration   41
11. Russian drilling performance and increase in production   44
12. Scheduled and actual production figures for the second Five-Year Plan, 1933-1937   46
13. Oil production of the Russian oil areas in 1938   47
14. Oil production scheduled for 1942   47
15. Oil production scheduled for 1950   49
16. Oil production in 1950   50
17. Crude oil processed in Russian refineries   53
18. Development of Russian oil exports in the decisive years from 1921 through 1938   55
19. Development of Russian oil consumption from 1929 to 1939   56
20. Oil consumption in the Soviet Union in 1937   60
21. Oil production in the Groznyy fields in 1938   73
22. Oil production in the Groznyy area from 1921 to 1940   73
23. Development of oil production in the Maykop area   74
24. Oil production in the Carpathian fields from 1930 to 1939   80
25. Oil and gas production in the Carpathian fields from 1941 to 1944   81
26. Development of the Estonian oil-shale industry between 1934 and 1939   84
27. Development of oil production in the Second Baku region   86

TABLES

28. Sakhalin crude-oil production 103
29. Contributions of the most important sources to the world energy supply, in percentages of the total 110
30. Contributions of the most important sources to the energy supply of the United States, in percentages of the total 111
31. Production of oil in the world, the United States, and the USSR between 1910 and 1950 112
32. Increase in population of some Russian cities 118
33. Development of oil production in countries with an uncontrolled oil industry 124
34. Development of oil production in countries with a state-controlled oil industry 124
35. Steel demand of the American oil industry in 1950 130
36. Development of oil production in Rumania 134
37. Russian crude-oil production, 1861-1950, compared with world and American crude-oil production 147
38. World crude-oil production, 1948-1950 149
39. Terms for various oil products 150
40. Classification of reserves of mineral deposits according to the decree of the Council of the People's Commissars of the Soviet Union, February 14, 1951 151
41. World oil production, 1950-1951 155
42. Basic production 156
43. Per-capita production 156

PART I

THE BASIS OF THE RUSSIAN OIL INDUSTRY

THE BASIS OF THE RUSSIAN
OIL INDUSTRY

THE philosophy of the political organism stretching from the Baltic Sea and the Bug River over the vast expanse of Eastern Europe and the steppes and deserts of Asia to the Pacific Ocean is difficult to understand for all who live outside its territory and are unaffected by its way of life. Russia is now, as in centuries past, an enigma. As a result, the usual conception of it is clouded, and opinions about it are inconsistent: there was Russia, a patriarchal czarist empire, and there is the Soviet Union, a council (soviet) of modern states.

However, though the mind of the Russian people and the philosophy of Bolshevism remain a mystery to us, the physical existence of the Soviet Union is subject to exact investigation and evaluation. Her economic and political life is carried on in outward forms and classifications that can be measured and understood in figures. The Russian economic region and system, as the basis for the Russian oil industry, definitely can be recognized, delineated, and described.

THE RUSSIAN ECONOMIC REGION

Territory

The Soviet Union, with an area of approximately nine million square miles, is the most compact territorial and political unit on earth. Three times as large as the United States, it covers one sixth of the continental surface of the globe. The greatest east-west distance is almost 6,200 miles and the greatest north-south distance almost 3,000 miles. The immensity of the Russian area is more comprehensible when it is realized that its northernmost point lies in Franz-Josef Land near the North Pole and its southernmost point lies on the borders of Afghanistan, on a line with North Africa. When night falls in the West of the Soviet Union a new day dawns in the East. The boundaries of this giant realm total about 36,000 miles, one and one half times the circumference of the earth at the equator. The Soviet Union borders upon nine seas and eleven countries. What a multitude of problems and opportunities can result from contiguity with so many nations!

The enormous Russian nation shows great variations in topography

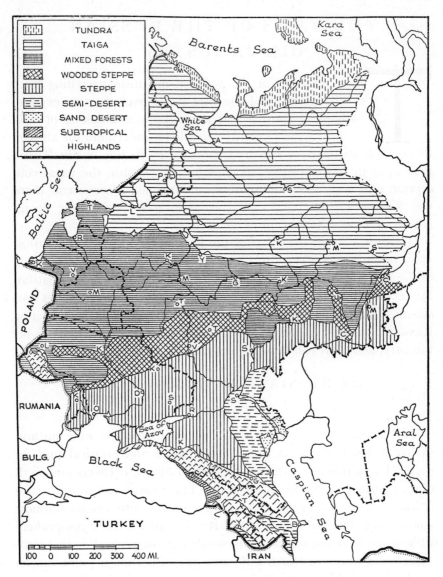

Fig. 1. Vegetation zones of the European USSR.

Reproduced from Shabad, *Geography of the USSR*
(New York: Columbia University Press, 1951).

and climate. The northernmost parts extend into the Arctic zone, while the regions on the southern boundaries of the Union are sub-tropical. Between the two lie the wide, treeless, moss-covered tundra on the coast of the Arctic Ocean, the broad forest belt that covers

FIG. 2. Vegetation zones of the Asiatic USSR.

Reproduced from Shabad, *Geography of the USSR* (New York: Columbia University Press, 1951).

about half the territory of the Union, and the steppes of the West which include Russia's most fertile region.[1] There is also some desert country where farming is possible only through irrigation. The Soviet Union has the world's largest area of arable soil, about 400 million acres, and the richest forests, covering about 2,375,000,000 acres.

This inconceivably vast expanse makes us throw overboard the conventional division of the globe into continents. The Bolshevists have

[1] Translator's note: See L. S. Berg, *Natural Regions of the USSR*, trans. O. A. Titelbaum (New York, 1950), pp. 9ff.

[5]

built up an empire with European as well as Asiatic traits, but it can be called neither "European" nor "Asiatic." The expression "Eurasian" seems the most adequate to describe the location and expanse of this gigantic territory, and is gaining more and more popularity.[2]

Population

Today the Soviet Union has a population in excess of 200 million people, ranking third after China and India. This population is not a homogeneous entity, shaped and molded into a unified race by common environment, but a community of about 60 different peoples and 100 smaller tribes, which vary greatly in numbers and civilization. The largest group is Slavic and includes the Great Russians, the Ukrainians, and the White Russians. This group makes up almost three fourths of the total population of the Soviet Union and is composed of a majority of Great Russians, who number about 100 million. The group second in size is the so-called Turkic peoples, who include the Uzbeks, Tatars, Cossacks, Azerbaijani, Kirghiz, and Turkmen. The third group, numerically, includes a considerable number of minorities, such as the Georgians, Armenians, Germans, Jews, Tadzhiks, and, since 1945, the Estonians, Latvians, and Lithuanians.[3]

Census figures for the last 50 years reflect the healthy birth rate of the nation. Russia's total population was 106 million in 1897, 147 million in 1926, and 170 million in 1939. It was estimated for voting purposes at 201 million in January 1950. This is almost twice the population of 1897. Assuming an annual growth at the rate of two to two and one half million people, the total number of Russian citizens will reach 230 million in 1960. This favorable demographic condition has enabled the Soviet Union to develop its distant, sparsely populated regions beyond the Urals.

History

Russia's history covers 11 centuries. There are four distinct epochs, each of which coincides with a change of the country's capital. Thus we find Kiev, Moscow, Saint Petersburg (now Leningrad), and, again, Moscow the successive centers of the Russian Empire.[4]

2 See Werner Leimbach, *Die Sowjetunion, Natur, Volk und Wirtschaft* (Stuttgart, 1950), and N. Michailov, *Reise über die Karte der Sowjetunion* (Berlin, 1947), especially pp. 47ff. (Translator's note: See bibliography for further literature.)

3 See Werner Leimbach, *op.cit.*, especially pp. 163ff.

4 See Otto Hoetzsch, *Grundzüge der Geschichte Russlands* (Stuttgart, 1949); Eugen Lemberg, *Osteuropa und die Sowjetunion* (Stuttgart, 1950); W. Klintshevsky, *Geschichte Russlands* (Stuttgart, 1925); Valentin Gitermann, *Geschichte Russlands* (Hamburg, 1949).

The most important event in its long and checkered history was Russia's expansion beyond the Urals into northern Asia, which eventually resulted in the incorporation of all of Siberia to the Bering Strait. This extension to the east began in the sixteenth century under Ivan IV, a remarkable ruler who is appreciated even by Soviet historians.[5]

A second event of great significance was Russia's contact with the West, which manifested itself in the reception of West European civilization, technology, and industrial methods, and, on the other hand, in the steadily increasing influence of Russia on European policies. The most prominent figures of this, the so-called Petersburg age, which began in 1689 and ended in 1917 with the collapse of the czarist regime, were Peter I and Catherine II, who made Russia a great power.

However, the most incisive impact on Russian history was that of the October Revolution of 1917, with the establishment of the Soviet state and the realization of socialism in the special Russian version of "Lenin-Stalinism." This meant a complete break with the past and initiated an entirely new development in Russian history. Russia's growth in the 30 years following the October Revolution altered it altogether from what it was in czarist times.

Today, in the middle of the twentieth century, Stalin, as head of the Soviet Union, wields immediate and almost unrestricted power over 200 million citizens of Soviet Russia, plus 700 million people of Asia and Europe. They are, in varying degrees, tied to the Soviet Union politically, economically, and ideologically. Thus Moscow has become a center of gravity as a world power, its only adversary of equal strength being the United States.

Constitution

The Constitution of Soviet Russia is based essentially upon two principles: the one-party system and the soviet principle.[6]

Basically, only one party is permitted in the Soviet Union, the "Communist party of the Bolsheviki." It is the sole representation of political power and the only reservoir of political energies. Its totalitarian position is chiefly the conception and work of Lenin, who, in

[5] See R. J. Vipper, *Ivan Grosnyy* (Moscow, 1946).
[6] See the excellent treatise by Boris Meissner in *Die Verfassungen der modernen Staaten* (Hamburg, 1947), and the article by the same author, "Stalinistische Autokratie und Bolschewistische Staatspartei" in *Europa-Archiv*, 1951, Nos. 4 and 5, pp. 3735ff.

his teachings on the party, called it "the summit of the organization of the working class."[7] With no party but the Communist permitted in the Soviet Union, opposing opinions are silenced.

Lenin built up his state on the soviet (council) system.[8] The Soviet Union is not a parliamentary republic but a republic of soviets; that is, of soviets of the workers and peasants, the two allied classes in Soviet society. Typical of this kind of political organization is the fact that you have three ranks of soviets. At the bottom is the lower or primary rank, from which one may advance to the middle rank, and then to the highest rank of soviets. The top of the organization is the Supreme Soviet of the Soviet Union, which is elected by the citizens of the Soviet Union.

This Supreme Soviet of the Soviet Union[9] consists of two chambers with equal rights, the Soviet of the Union, with 671 deputies at present, and the Soviet of the Nationalities, with 631 deputies at present. The Supreme Soviet, that is, the parliament, chooses a Presidium whose chairman performs the duties of titular head of the state, and a Council of Ministers, the highest executive and administrative organ, or the government, of the Soviet Union. The Council of Ministers is charged with carrying out the laws enacted by the Supreme Soviet and governing the state. Stalin has been chairman of the Council of Ministers since May 7, 1941.[10]

Organic unity and solidarity are guaranteed by so-called "democratic centralism,"[10a] the essential elements of which are the ideas of the rule of the majority and subordination. The idea of majority rule means that the minority owes blind obedience to the majority.

[7] The organization and function of the Communist party can be gathered from Lenin's publication (1904), "One Step Forward, Two Steps Backward," contained in V. I. Lenin, *Selected Writings* (Moscow, 1946). See also *Geschichte der Kommunistischen Partei der Sowjetunion (Bolschewiki), Kurzer Lehrgang* (Berlin, 1949), especially pp. 63ff.

[8] On the origin of the soviets, see *Geschichte der Kommunistischen Partei, op.cit.,* pp. 106ff., 239, 250.

[9] See *ibid.,* pp. 466ff., and the Constitution of the Soviet Union of 1936.

[10] Translator's note: The Soviet power structure after Stalin's death (March 5, 1953) in the order of importance of the various organs: Presidium of the Central Committee of the Communist Party; Secretariat of the Central Committee of the Communist Party; Council of Ministers; Supreme Soviet. The *New York Times,* March 9, 1953, p. 5.

[10a] According to *Geschichte der Kommunistischen Partei, op.cit.,* p. 268, "democratic centralism" means:
   a) Eligibility of all leading organs of the party from the top to the bottom.
   b) Periodical accounting of party divisions to their party organizations.
   c) Rigid party discipline and obedience of the minority to the majority.
   d) Directions of the higher organs to the lower organs and all party members are absolutely binding.

The idea of subordination is that the directions of the higher organs are absolutely binding on the lower ranks of the party.

These guiding principles have found their legal expression in the political constitutions of the individual Soviet republics and the Soviet Union proper, representing all of the Soviet republics. The first constitution of any Soviet republic was that of July 10, 1918, of the Russian Soviet Federated Socialist Republic (RSFSR), by far the most important federal state of the present union. The first constitution of the Soviet Union as a whole was dated July 6, 1923. It has been replaced by a new constitution dated December 5, 1936, the so-called "Stalin constitution," which is still in effect with minor changes.

The Soviet Union itself is a union of sixteen constituent Soviet Socialist Republics (SSR), as follows:

Republic	Capital
Russian SFSR	Moscow
Ukrainian SSR	Kiev
Belorussian SSR	Minsk
Azerbaijan SSR	Baku
Georgian SSR	Tbilisi
Armenian SSR	Erivan
Turkmen SSR	Ashkhabad
Uzbek SSR	Tashkent
Tadzhik SSR	Stalinabad
Kazakh SSR	Alma-Ata
Kirghiz SSR	Frunze
Karelo-Finnish SSR	Petrozavodsk
Moldavian SSR	Kishinev
Lithuanian SSR	Vilna
Latvian SSR	Riga
Estonian SSR	Tallin

Economy

Just as the October (1917) Revolution divides Russian history into czarist and Soviet epochs, it also marks the beginning of a new economy.[11]

Before 1917 Russia was an agrarian state which, even after the abolition of serfdom in the 1860's, had not lost all of its patriarchal

[11] See Adolf Weber, *Marktwirtschaft und Sowjetwirtschaft* (Munich, 1949), and *Dogma und Wirklichkeitssinn in der Sowjetwirtschaft* (Munich, 1950), by the same author.

feudalistic traits. Western capitalism did not emerge in Russia until the second half of the last century and not to a marked degree until 1890. The number of industrial workers increased from 700,000 to 1,400,000 between 1865 and 1890, and to 2,800,000 between 1890 and 1900. Still, industrialization in Russia did not reach the importance it had gained in Germany and England. At the turn of the century five sixths of the population were employed in agriculture and only one sixth in other pursuits. Industrialization was limited to a few fields that within the framework of the Russian economy had the appearance of something foreign, well-nigh alien, and was largely dominated by foreign capital.

The October Revolution ushered in an entirely new era. An event of decisive importance was the introduction of modern technology. Taken over from the West in a highly developed form, it was to become one of the strongest forces in the transformation of the country.[12]

The Revolution effected industrialization of the economy, motorization of transportation, and mechanization of agriculture, and introduced modern, technical weapons on a large scale in the Soviet army. In an unusually brief period of three decades the entire economic structure of the country has been fundamentally changed. Where in czarist rule about 67 per cent of the national income was derived from agriculture, in 1929-1930 industry, with 53 per cent, surpassed agriculture in national production and steadily outdistanced it in the following years.[13]

This industrial development, however, was not achieved under the capitalistic system typical of the West, but under a new economic theory evolved from Marxist theories by the Soviets.

THE RUSSIAN ECONOMIC SYSTEM

Soviet Economic Theory

The basis of the Soviet Russian political and economic system is "dialectical and historical materialism," a philosophical doctrine elaborated by Karl Marx and Friedrich Engels and built into a comprehensive social system by V. I. Lenin and Joseph Stalin.[14] This system is based upon the philosophical concepts "materialism" and

---

[12] See *Geschichte der Kommunistischen Partei, op.cit.*, pp. 422ff.

[13] See *ibid.*, p. 420.

[14] See *ibid.*, pp. 141-179, and Adolf Weber, *Dogma und Wirklichkeitssinn, op.cit.*, pp. 16ff.

"dialectic." The synthesis of materialism and dialectic produced a new orientation referred to by Marx as "historical materialism," which he used as a tool to investigate society and its history.

It is a fundamental presupposition of materialistic philosophy that material life has precedence over spiritual life. Opposed to idealism, which sees in the world the embodiment of an idea, materialism considers an idea a function of matter. All sensations, concepts, and comprehensions are traced back to matter, which is the only reality. "The material life of society is the primary, the original, source; spiritual life is secondary, is derivative."[15]

Dialectic does not regard all recognizable appearances and facts as something static and fixed but as the result of reciprocal action of opposing forces. The dialectic method concludes, according to Lenin, that "developments do not unfold harmoniously but emerge from a struggle of opposite tendencies. . . . Development is the struggle of opposing principles."[16]

The "historical materialism" of Marx derives from the earlier philosophical materialism the view that in history, too, material facts and not spiritual things are prime movers. While Marx does not deny that social ideas and political opinions have a certain bearing on the course of history, still these factors are not the original causes but are derived from material events. Furthermore, "historical materialism" holds that the dialectical analysis is not limited merely to the study of nature but must be utilized in the study of history. For changes in history are manifestations of the struggle between conflicting forces. The great conflicts in history basically involve conditions of the material life of society. These material conditions of life emerge from the fear of not being able to make a living. The main concern of Soviet economic theory is with earning the means for a livelihood; that is, with the method of producing goods. This is, according to historical materialism and, consequently, to Soviet economic thought, the main factor in the development of human society. Because "as is the method of producing goods in a given society, so is essentially the society itself, its ideas and theories, its political opinions and institutions."[17]

As the production methods, so the way of living; as the way of living, so the way of thinking.

[15] *Geschichte der Kommunistischen Partei, op.cit.,* p. 155.
[16] *ibid.,* p. 147.
[17] *ibid.,* p. 164.

The method of producing goods is determined by the conditions of employment. In order to produce, not only the means of production are needed—land, raw materials, buildings—but also men to employ these means. The relationship of the workmen to the means of production is called conditions of employment. The Soviet economic theory concentrates logically on the exploration of the conditions of employment.

In the capitalistic system, conditions of employment are characterized by the contrast between the ruling class, owning the means of production, and the exploited class, which is excluded from ownership. The abolition of these conditions through transfer of the means of production to the people is the salient claim of Soviet economic theory. This change of conditions of employment also basically transforms the structure of society. The transformation from the capitalistic order to the socialistic order of society can be attained only through a change of the conditions of employment.

In detail, Soviet economic thought considers the following four measures necessary to transform the former capitalistic conditions of employment into the socialistic order of society:

1. Socialization; that is, the transfer of soil, subsoil resources, and plants from their private owners to the community.

2. Collectivization; that is, the transfer of farm lands from private owners to social organizations.

3. Industrialization; that is, the establishment of a socialistic heavy industry to give "capitalism the death blow economically."

4. Introduction of a planned economy; that is, the management of the socialized, collectivistic, and industrialized economy according to a uniform plan aiming at the final elimination of the law of the market.

Economic Provisions of the Soviet Constitution

These goals are anchored in the Constitution of the Union of Soviet Socialist Republics of 1936. According to Article 4 of the Constitution, the whole economic structure of the USSR rests upon the "socialist economic system." Hand in hand with the abolition of private ownership of the means of production, socialistic ownership was established; that is, either state, cooperative, or collectivistic ownership of property. According to Article 6 of the Constitution, state property includes, among other things, the soil with its mineral resources, factories, and mines with mining installations. Coopera-

tive property is collective farms and cooperative organizations with livestock, equipment, and produce, according to Article 7. In addition to state and cooperative property, there is limited private or personal property which is legally protected, as is the right of inheritance of this property, according to Article 10 of the Constitution.

According to Article 11 of the Constitution, through State Economic Plans the entire economic life of the Soviet Union is determined by, and managed in, the interest of increasing the prosperity of society, constantly improving the material and cultural level of the workers, strengthening the independence of the USSR, and advancing the preparedness of its armed forces. The State Economic Plans project total production and consumption in the Soviet Union for five years, and supplant the role of free competition in a free enterprise system.

The realization of these two principles, socialization of the means of production and management of the economy according to a total plan, revolutionized economic conditions in the Soviet Union. The free market economy, undisputed before World War I, was replaced by the new system of a state-planned economy that does not exempt any field of human endeavor or commercial transaction.

While a free market economy considers the market as a scale which automatically restores the equilibrium between production and consumption, or between supply and demand, within a state-planned economy the government exercises this function. The state decides the kind and volume of production. By exercise of its powers the state is in a position to achieve complete coordination of the entire economic life and to direct all forces toward attainment of the desired goals. All economic transactions are decided upon by the government. It determines production, provides manpower, raw materials, and finances, and, finally, arranges for distribution of manufactured goods to the ultimate consumer. Producers, dealers, and consumers depend upon the economic guidance of the government. A free market economy is directed from the base up, while a planned state economy is managed from the top down.

Where, in a free market economy, free competition provides incentive and guarantees efficiency, a planned economy endeavors to solve the problem differently. As early as 1931 Stalin opposed lack of incentive in a spectacular address.[18] Today the principle of effi-

18 See Lemberg, *op.cit.,* p. 190.

ciency plays a decisive part in the Soviet Union. The institution of socialistic contests[19] such as the Stakhanov system[20] and the recognition of piecework[21] and piecework pay are the most important features intended to stimulative incentive and efficiency in the Soviet economy.

Various Periods of the Soviet Economy

The October Revolution of 1917 by no means found a ready-made program for a government-planned economy. This assumed its present shape only after many years and not without long and violent arguments. Three periods of development can be distinguished:

1. *The period of war communism, 1917-1921.*[22] The victorious October Revolution of 1917 ordered the expropriation of land and farming, without indemnification, in its Decree of Land and Farming of October 26 (November 8), 1917.[23] This measure was followed by nationalization of heavy industry, the banks, railroads, merchant marine, and commercial shipping. But the new socialistic setup suffered from the beginning from the aftermath of World War I and the difficulties brought about by civil war and foreign intervention, which seriously threatened the newly established social order. In this tense situation war communism was born. It is marked by a number of radical steps. The large, medium-sized, and small industries were put under government control, total production was registered, and consumption rationed. A grain monopoly was introduced. The farmers were forced to surrender their produce and compulsory labor was established. Strong countermovements, engendered by these stringent measures, caused Lenin to take a wide turn and to shift from war communism to the so-called New Economic Policy.

2. *The period of the New Economic Policy (NEP), 1921-1927.*[24] The New Economic Policy, which was decreed by the tenth convention of the Communist party in March 1921, was a retreat to a cer-

---

[19] See *Geschichte der Kommunistischen Partei, op.cit.*, p. 402; Adolf Weber, *Dogma und Wirklichkeitssinn, op.cit.*, p. 35.

[20] See *Geschichte der Kommunistischen Partei, op.cit.*, p. 457.

[21] See Lemberg, *op.cit.*, p. 190.

[22] See *Geschichte der Kommunistischen Partei, op.cit.*, p. 310; Lemberg, *op.cit.*, pp. 174ff.; Hoetzsch, *op.cit.*, pp. 178ff.

[23] For the text of the decree see Gitermann, *op.cit.*, III, 635.

[24] See *Geschichte der Kommunistischen Partei, op.cit.*, pp. 336, 346; Lemberg, *op.cit.*, pp. 178ff.; Hoetzsch, *op.cit.*, pp. 183ff.; Adolf Weber, *Dogma und Wirklichkeitssin, op.cit.*, p. 13, where the famous definition of the NEP by Stalin is found. (Translator's note: An authoritative book in English on the NEP is Alexander Baykov's *The Development of the Soviet Economic System* [Cambridge, Eng., 1946].)

tain degree. The heavy and other key industries, the banks, and the railroads remained socialized, but peasant property was restored, private trade was readmitted, and private entrepreneurs were permitted to open or reopen small industrial plants. This new economic policy was successful to the extent that the grant of personal freedom and the appeal to private initiative produced an immediate revival of, and increase in, agricultural and industrial production.

However, a year later, in March 1922, Lenin declared at the eleventh convention of the Communist party, "We have been retreating for one year. Now we must say in behalf of the party: Enough! The goal of the retreat has been reached; this period is approaching an end or has come to an end. Now we set ourselves another aim: to regroup our forces."[25] Still, the principles of the NEP governed the economic policy of the Soviet Union for a few more years. Not until the fourteenth convention in December 1925 did the state-planned economy come to the fore again. With it the Soviet Union launched its third economic period, a period of a state-planned economy expanding more and more.

3. *The period of a state-planned economy since 1928.* The idea of state control of all economic transactions, based on an over-all plan, emanated from the total socialization of the means of production. The state-planned economy found its most distinct expression in the institution of the Five-Year Plans.

The first Five-Year Plan (1928-1932) was directed chiefly toward the expansion of heavy industry and electric power, the modernization of transportation, and the collectivization and mechanization of agriculture. At its end industrial production had taken precedence over agricultural production; 70 per cent of the total production was achieved by industry.

The second Five-Year Plan (1933-1937) emphasized the continuation of collectivization and mechanization of agriculture, and the technical improvement of transportation and communication. By the end of this plan the collectivization of agriculture was completed. Industry, transportation, and the Red army had new machinery and modern technical equipment.

The third Five-Year Plan (1938-1942) was interrupted by the calamity of the Russo-German war in 1941. It is known as the Five-Year Plan of chemistry. Apart from the continued improvement of

[25] Quoted in *Geschichte der Kommunistischen Partei, op.cit.,* p. 351.

the transportation system, mechanization of farming, and development of heavy industry, its chief interest was devoted to the advancement of petroleum, coal, lumber, and metallurgical chemistry.

The fourth Five-Year Plan (1946-1950) had for its main task the repair of damage wrought by the war in occupied areas, and the restoration of prewar production in farming and industry. Scheduled production figures for 1950, the last year of the fourth Five-Year Plan, were:[26]

Motor vehicles	0.5	million vehicles
Iron	19.5	million tons
Steel	25.4	million tons
Petroleum	35.4	million tons
Coal	250.0	million tons
Natural gas	296.6	billion cubic feet
Electric power	82.0	billion kilowatt-hours

The fifth Five-Year Plan (1951-1955) will be published in 1951. It will probably continue mechanization of agriculture, motorization of transportation, and industrialization in general, and attach great importance to the economic development of Asiatic territories, especially Kazakhstan and West Siberia. It is absolutely certain that rearmament will have precedence over everything else. The underlying idea of all the Five-Year Plans is to firmly establish Soviet superiority —to catch up with, and to surpass, the accomplishments of capitalistic Western society. Stalin said in 1925, "The essence, the basis of our immediate policy is to change our agrarian country into an industrial country which will use its capacity to take care of our needs."[27] This aim, established 25 years ago, is, thanks to the Five-Year Plans, regarded as fulfilled to a considerable extent.

Soviet Economic Achievements[28]

The success of the Five-Year Plans cannot be denied. The Soviet economic achievements are particularly impressive in the expansion

[26] See the report of N. A. Vosnessenskij, chairman of the State Planning Commission, on the meeting of the Supreme Soviet of the USSR, published in Berlin in 1946. (Translator's note: For latest figures, see infra, pp. 18, 156.)

[27] Quoted in *Geschichte der Kommunistischen Partei, op.cit.,* p. 373.

[28] See Lemberg, *op.cit.,* p. 188: "First of all it must be said that under the Five-Year Plans a tremendous work of reconstruction has been achieved. The face and character of an entire continent have been fundamentally changed. The scope and tempo of industrialization have dwarfed anything known so far, even though industrialization had begun to a certain degree during czarist rule." Also Adolf Weber, *Dogma und*

of existing, and establishment of new, industrial areas, which are to-day the backbone of the Russian economic potential.

While light industry is not much restricted in location because its raw materials are widely distributed, heavy industry is definitely tied to fixed localities. Its location depends largely upon the existence of the mineral resources upon which it is based. For instance, it is dependent upon deposits of iron and nonferrous ores, oil and potash, and fuel and water power reserves. Wherever these conditions were found the Soviet government took the initiative and built centers of heavy industry. It created areas of heavy industry where coal mines, ore mines, oil fields, blast furnaces, steel and rolling mills, heating systems, and hydroelectric power stations were concentrated; as well as shipyards and factories, where machinery, tools, locomotives, freight cars, automobiles, and trucks are being manufactured.

The economic potential of the Soviet Union is based today on the following industrial areas, which are listed, not in the order of their economic importance, but of their geographical location:

1. The industrial area of the European Northwest, with Leningrad as its center.

2. The Central Russian industrial district. It lies in a wide circle around Moscow and contains the rich lignite deposits of the Moscow Basin.

3. The South Russian industrial area, in the Donets and Dnieper Basins, with the bituminous coal deposits of the Donets region and the iron ore of Krivoi Rog.

4. The industrial area of the Middle Volga, which extends from Kazan in the north to Stalingrad in the south. This area has important oil and natural-gas deposits.

5. The industrial area of the Urals, with Nizhniy Tagil, Sverdlovsk, Chelyabinsk, and Magnitogorsk as central points, possessing rich ore and potash deposits.

6. The industrial area of the Caucasus, between Novorossiysk in the northwest and Baku in the southeast, the most important feature of which is the rich oil deposits.

7. The Kuznetsk area, lying in a rectangle between the cities of Novosibirsk, Barnaul, Stalinsk, and Tomsk, with important coal deposits.

Wirklichkeitssin, op.cit., p. 32: "One must confess that the Soviet economy has made great progress in the development of the factors of production which are at its disposal (labor, land, capital)."

8. The industrial area around Lake Baikal, with coal deposits. Irkutsk is the focal point.

9. The industrial area in the Far East, located on both banks of the Amur River, with Khabarovsk and Komsomolsk as centers.

10. The industrial area in Central Asia, between Tashkent and Alma-Ata, with rich coal, iron, and oil deposits.

These ten industrial regions show the intensity of the Soviet economic reconstruction. A survey of the production and processing of raw materials from these areas, and of the utilization of natural power, supplements this brief review of the Soviet economy, as follows:

TABLE 1. Survey of Soviet Production[29]

Year	Coal	Pig Iron (millions of tons)	Steel	Oil	Electric Current (billions of kilowatt-hours)
1913	29	4.2	4.2	8.7	2.0
1938	133	14.6	18.0	28.2	39.4
1949	237	17.2	21.0	33.2	74.2
1950	261	19.5	27.0	37.6	90.0
1960 (scheduled)	500	50.0	60.0	60.0	......

[29] Translator's note: Harry Schwartz in the *New York Times*, February 1, 1952, gave his analysis of the 1951 Soviet economic report, which is printed below. "Data is expressed in millions of short tons, millions of pairs, billions of yards, billions of kilowatt-hours or millions of individuals, as appropriate."

Product	1940	1950	1951
Pig iron	16.5	21.2	24.2
Steel	20.1	30.0	34.5
Coal	182.6	290.4	313.6
Petroleum	34.1	41.3	45.2
Cement	6.4	11.4	13.6
Electric power	48.3	90.3	102.9
Leather shoes	230.0	197.0	230.5
Hosiery	480.0	430.0	542.0
Cotton cloth	4.4	4.3	5.2
Grain (there were substantial harvest losses and other losses)	131.0	136.0	133.0
Sugar beets (there were substantial harvest losses and other losses)	23.0	25.7	29.7
Cattle	54.5	57.2	58.8
Hogs	27.5	24.1	26.7
Sheep and goats	91.6	99.0	117.5
Labor force (exclusive of collective farms and prison workers)	31.2	39.2	40.8

PART II

THE DEVELOPMENT OF THE RUSSIAN OIL INDUSTRY

THE DEVELOPMENT OF THE RUSSIAN
OIL INDUSTRY

Russia is one of the world's most important oil countries! At the end of its first 40 years of commercial oil production, 1860-1900, Russia's production had climbed as high as that of the United States, which had held first place in the world oil industry for 50 years. Around the turn of the century, Russia succeeded in producing *more* oil than the United States. From 1902 on Russia was in second place, and since 1945 has been in third place, after Venezuela, which became the world's second largest producer of oil.

A curve of Russian production shows that it increased from about 1,000 tons in 1860 to 37,600,000 tons in 1950. This curve, however, is not straight. Three rather deep notches indicate a decline in production in 1905 to 1909, 1918 to 1925, and 1945 to 1947, caused in each case by circumstances other than economic. The decrease in production in 1905 was the result of political riots in the Baku region on account of the unfortunate outcome of the Russo-Japanese war. The decline in oil production between 1918 and 1925 emanated from the 1917 Revolution, civil war, and foreign intervention. The drop between 1945 and 1947 was due to the damage and extraordinary drain of the Second World War. (See statistics in the appendix.)

The year 1917 played an incisive role in all of the Russian economy, as in the Russian oil industry. The attitude of the imperial state differed basically from that of the Soviet political and economic regime.

THE DEVELOPMENT OF THE CZARIST
OIL INDUSTRY

The roots of Russian oil history reach far back to the realm of ancient myths—for instance, the reports of the Cloister of the Eternal Fire, which stood at Surakhany on the Apsheron Peninsula. Today they have for us only historical interest. Legally, the Russian oil problem first became acute in the 1820's when the Russian government, to increase its revenues, declared the exploitation of oil a state monopoly. However, Russian oil did not gain economic importance until commercial production began in the second half of the nineteenth century. Therefore, our historical survey is limited to those six decades which lie between 1860 and 1917.[1]

The Czarist Empire and the Oil Industry

Experience in oil countries of the world during the last decades has taught that steady progress in the oil industry does not depend alone on technical perfection of methods of production and processing, and the status of scientific research in geology and geophysics. Just as important as the work of science and technology is the government's attitude toward the oil industry, as expressed in its legislation. Farsighted laws in favor of private economy encourage and support development in the oil industry. Intentionally or unintentionally hostile legislation hampers sound progress, furthers uneconomic waste, and may even lead to a complete breakdown of the oil industry in question.

The czarist government was lacking in such foresight, which is essential to the oil industry. Shortsighted, motivated by egotistic considerations and policies, it made the establishment of a healthy Russian oil industry unnecessarily difficult. Its attitude toward the problems of the infant industry was not uniform, but the underlying issue of any new legislation was the securing of new sources of revenue for the treasury.

The lease system, 1821-1872: From 1821 to 1872, Russia employed the so-called lease system. The government, which made the exploitation of oil deposits a state monopoly, leased the oil fields to individual entrepreneurs. Since the fields were leased for only four years, this system was exceedingly disadvantageous. The poor drilling methods of the day absorbed a considerable portion of the entire term of the lease in getting wells drilled, and left only a short time for production proper. This system was more of an obstacle than an encouragement to the lessees. Consequently, it is understandable that results were poor. The government received from these leases, between 1821 and 1872, a total of only 3.74 million rubles, or about three million gold dollars (1914 value).

The auction system from 1872 to 1896: The state monopoly was abolished in 1872. The oil fields, over which the government had the right of disposition, could now be turned over to private owners.

---

[1] On the development of the czarist oil industry, see the essay by W. von Knorre, "Die russische Erdölwirtschaft" in *Petroleum* (Vienna, 1927). The author based his figures on Dr. von Knorre's treatise.

They were awarded by public auction to the highest bidders. However, the government did not allow the acquisition of the properties as complete geological units, but divided them into small parcels of two and one-half to ten acres and auctioned them individually. This made large-scale operation impossible. The parcels were too small to permit orderly recovery and production. Furthermore, the various fields of individual producers were too widely separated to permit unified technical management and sensible economic employment of machinery and equipment. The result was a reckless waste which spared neither the operator's fields nor his neighbors'.

The combined auction and royalty system from 1896 to 1917: This auction system was changed in the 1890's. The government, in the interest of higher revenues, demanded not only the auction price but a current royalty based on a percentage of production, to be paid in currency or in kind. This selfish attitude of the state burdened production with unhealthy levies, which sometimes amounted to as much as 40 per cent of production. As a result, Russian oil production fell more and more behind the production of the United States after the turn of the century. This decline in Russian production stemmed from legislation which showed little understanding of the economic needs of the oil industry. This attitude of the government is even less comprehensible in light of the fact that it, as the owner of the railroads and other transportation, was an important consumer of oil products.

Oil Areas and Oil Production in
Czarist Times

Before the October 1917 Revolution, with the exception of negligible production in the Fergana Valley, in Central Asia, and on Sakhalin Island in the Far East, oil was produced in commercially substantial quantities only in Baku, Groznyy, Maykop, and the Emba region, and on Cheleken Island.

The Baku area: Then, as today, Baku, located on the Apsheron Peninsula, which projects into the Caspian Sea, held first rank among all Russian oil regions. The oldest oil fields of this area are, north of Baku, Sabunchi, Balakhany, and Romany, which have been producing since the 1870's, and, south of Baku, the field of Bibi-Eybat, which started producing in 1882. Shortly after the turn of the century the Binagady and Surakhany fields were added to the list of these four famous fields. The tremendous yield of these six fields put Baku in undisputed lead in the Russian oil industry and the oil industry of the world at large. In 1909 and 1910 Baku produced more than eight million tons of crude oil annually.

The special significance of the Baku area is due to:

1. A great wealth of oil in its subsoil, which places it in line with the world's great oil provinces. It has 22 oil horizons capable of commercial production.

2. The small geographical extent of this oil district, which occupies only a comparatively small part of the Apsheron Peninsula.

Concentration of the oil deposits in such a narrow space facilitates the discovery and production of the deposits, but, on the other hand, makes for waste, since little technical effort or careful treatment is required.

3. The fact that many "gushers"[2] were drilled played an important role in the history of Baku oil production. In 1895 there were not less than 42 gushers producing, with an annual output of 1,853,000 tons. In 1901 there were 35 gushers, with a production of about 1,607,000 tons. The most famous of these gushers, spouting in some cases as high as 233 feet, was in Bibi-Eybat; it produced in a single month in 1882 about 480,000 tons of oil. The discovery of such gushers frequently resulted in large land speculations, which disturbed the normal development of the Baku oil industry.

The oil district of Groznyy: The oil district of Groznyy, which is still producing, was, next to Baku, the most important oil area of the Russian Empire. It lies around the city of Groznyy, on the northeast slope of the Caucasus Mountains, about 100 miles from the Caspian Sea. Its most important fields are:

1. The Old Groznyy field, northwest of the city of Groznyy, the oldest field in the area. Here oil was produced from shallow wells as early as 1833. Commercial production was, however, not started until 1893, when the first gusher was drilled.

2. The New Groznyy field, south of Groznyy, discovered in 1913. Of 22 sandstone horizons in succession, 13 have proved petroliferous. The remaining nine were not productive. In 1910 production of the two Groznyy fields exceeded one million tons for the first time. (See Table 2.)

2 "Gushers" are wells from which the oil flows due to the high natural pressure of the reservoir. In the case of deposits that do not have that high natural pressure, the oil must be produced by means of pumps or bailing. It is obvious that flowing production requires less technical effort and that costs are also less.

The oil area of Maykop: The oil area of Maykop is on the northern slope of the western Caucasus Mountains, about 90 miles from the coast of the Black Sea. This area was also discovered by the drilling of a gusher in 1908. Its discovery and the expectations that followed led to the establishment of no less than 30 oil companies, most of them English, in the hope that Maykop would develop similarly to Baku. But production at Maykop was far less prolific: 1911 and 1912 showed a steep increase (to more than 100,000 tons annually) but from 1913 on production declined rapidly, and Maykop's role in czarist times, compared with Baku's and Groznyy's, was insignificant.

The Emba oil region: The Emba oil region lies on the north coast of the Caspian Sea. It is about 130 miles wide and stretches from the mouth of the Ural and Emba Rivers in a northeasterly direction. Production started in 1912, increased rapidly, and reached its peak in the czarist era in 1914, with a production of 274,000 tons. The promises of this area were not realized during the czarist regime.

The Cheleken Island oil area: Cheleken Island lies off the eastern coast of the Caspian Sea on a line with Baku. Here production began in 1909. It reached a peak of 200,000 tons annually in 1911 and 1912, and has declined steadily since 1913.

TABLE 2. Russian Oil Production from 1908 to 1916
(thousands of tons)

Year	Baku	Groznyy	Maykop	Emba	Cheleken
1908	7,570	850	1	......	......
1909	8,230	935	10	......	49
1910	8,230	1,210	21	......	157
1911	7,380	1,230	127	......	218
1912	7,720	1,070	151	16	213
1913	7,570	1,210	78	98	111
1914	6,950	1,610	66	274	82
1915	7,400	1,670	32	245	48
1916	7,820	1,560	32	265	16

Summary: A review of Russian oil production from 1860 on shows a regular increase in production until 1901, when it was at its peak of 12 million tons (more than 50 per cent of world production). From 1904 until 1917 it declined not only relatively—that is, compared with world production—but absolutely also. Within Russia, Baku remained supreme in oil production, as shown by a comparison of the several areas. Before World War I, the Russian oil industry was synonymous with Baku.

Oil Companies and Their Investments
in the Czarist Era

Before World War I about 320 companies were engaged in the production and processing of oil, the distribution of oil products, and the purchase and sale of oil concessions. Most of these companies were oil producers. Baku alone had 198 oil-producing companies in 1910. More than half the capital invested in these companies came from abroad.

The more important companies, in the wake of a general trend toward concentration, eventually formed three groups which decisively influenced the Russian oil industry. These were the Nobel concern, the Russian General Oil Corporation (RGOC), and the Royal Dutch-Shell group. They gradually succeeded in incorporating other important oil companies, such as the Lianosov and Mantashev groups.

The Nobel group: Credit for initiating and leading the Russian oil industry to world importance is due the brothers Robert and Ludwig (Lewis) Nobel, who immigrated with their father from Sweden to Russia. These men were experienced as technicians, organizers, and economists. They are rightly called the pioneers of the Russian oil industry. They built up an oil concern engaged in production, transportation, and distribution. In 1875 they acquired the oil field of Balakhany at Baku. In 1879 they founded the Naphtha Production Company Nobel Brothers Joint Stock Company (Société Anonyme d'Exploitation du Naphte Nobel Frères). By acquiring oil fields, modernizing technical operations, establishing modern refineries, and constructing efficient transportation and distribution systems, the concern firmly established itself as a leading factor among the Russian companies. In this connection it is worthy of mention that the Nobel Brothers built the first Russian pipeline between Baku oil fields and refineries, and put into operation the first Russian tanker, the *Zoroaster,* in 1877.

During World War I the Nobel concern acquired the majority of the stock of the Russian General Oil Corporation, second largest group in the Russian oil industry. This put the Nobel concern into first place in the Russian oil industry. The Nobel enterprises, along with the entire Russian industry, were nationalized after the 1917

Revolution. However, despite nationalization and expropriation, the shares maintained a high value abroad. A small block of the stock passed into English possession, but the bulk of it was taken up by the American Standard Oil group, which hoped to derive rights and claims from it at a later date.

The capital of the Nobel concern in 1914 was 43.4 million rubles, or about $23 million (gold), before acquisition of part of the shares of the RGOC.[3]

The Russian General Oil Corporation (RGOC): The Russian General Oil Corporation was founded in 1912 by Russian banks and industrialists, with considerable participation by London capital. It was essentially a financing and holding company. Most of the Russian oil companies, such as A. I. Mantashev, G. M. Lianosov, and the Neft, belonged to this group. The Neft separated from the RGOC when the Nobel Brothers gained control of RGOC during World War I. The share capital of RGOC before Nobel acquired it in 1914 was 123.2 million rubles, or about $66.5 million (gold).

The Royal Dutch-Shell group: The Parisian bank of the Rothschilds founded the Société Caspienne et de la Mer Noire in 1892. In 1912 the Royal Dutch-Shell group acquired by purchase the majority of the stock of this company, which gave it a foothold in the Russian oil industry. Shell owned, among other companies, the Shibajeff Company and Mazut, a transportation, storage, and trading company also established by the Rothschilds. The share capital of the Royal Dutch-Shell was 61.7 million rubles, or about $33 million (gold), in 1914.

The predominant position of these three groups is shown in the following table:

TABLE 3. Production of the Oil Companies of Russia from 1910 to 1914
(thousands of tons)

	1910	1911	1912	1913	1914
RGOC	2,724	2,309	2,280	2,185	1,977
Royal Dutch-Shell	1,260	1,324	1,262	1,297	1,513
Nobel	1,226	1,209	1,305	1,292	1,239
Total	5,210	4,842	4,847	4,774	4,729
Other Producers	4,470	4,266	4,514	4,480	4,493
Grand Total	9,680	9,108	9,361	9,254	9,222

[3] Translator's note: An interesting report on the oil industry in Russia and the operations of the Nobel concern is found in Charles Marvin's *The Region of the Eternal Fire* (London, 1888). It is still fascinating reading.

An examination of the capital structure of the Russian oil industry shows the astonishing fact that prior to 1917 more than half the capital came from abroad. The total amount invested in the Russian oil industry before 1914 was approximately $214 million. The Russian share of this amount was only about $85 million, while foreign investment in the industry amounted to about $130 million (gold). The distribution of the foreign capital by individual contributions is shown in Table 4:

TABLE 4. Foreign Investment in the Russian Oil Industry in 1914
(thousands of gold dollars [1914])

U.S.A.	620
Belgium	3,800
Netherlands	5,600
Germany	7,300
France	26,400
Great Britain	86,000
Total	129,720

Particularly conspicuous is the high British share in this foreign investment, which may have been due to Britain's intention of becoming independent of the United States in obtaining oil. This participation was chiefly through the Royal Dutch-Shell group and the Russian General Oil Corporation. It secured for Britain a dominant position in the Russian oil industry. British capital was invested in all of the Russian oil regions. (See Table 5.)

TABLE 5. Distribution of British Capital among Russian Oil Regions

Region	British Capital (millions of gold dollars [1914])	British Interest (per cent of total interest in region)
Baku	25.0	60
Emba	16.0	90
Groznyy	13.2	50
Maykop	12.4	90
Sakhalin	3.0	not known
Fergana Valley	2.5	" "
Others	13.1	" "
Total	85.2	

The French interests were established with the foundation of the Société Caspienne et de la Mer Noire, founded by the Rothschilds of Paris. The stock of this company was purchased by the Royal Dutch-Shell company in 1912; thus the Dutch interest was established in the Russian industry. German capital was limited to the Nobel concern. The participation of Belgium and the United States was small.

Oil Processing and Domestic Demand
in the Czarist Era

In czarist times by far the largest part of Russian production was consumed by the Russian market. Contrary to frequently voiced opinion, only a comparatively small part of Russian oil was shipped abroad. For instance, 78.7% of the Baku production in 1903 and 79.7% in 1913 were shipped into the interior of Russia, and only 21.3% and 20.3%, respectively, were shipped abroad. These figures confirm the preponderance of the Russian market. The reasons for the primary importance of Russian demand were not only domestic consumption, but also the transportation and freight policy of the Russian government, which deliberately diverted the flow of oil so that it remained in Russia.

In a modern industrialized state, gasoline, diesel oil, and lubricating oil are of paramount importance. Their consumption is an unmistakable indication of the extent of industrialization and motorization. The consumption of fuel oil and kerosene usually lags behind these products. However, in a predominantly agricultural economy, such as czarist Russia, fuel oil and, to a certain degree, kerosene are very important, while lubricating oil and gasoline fall far behind.

Fuel oil: Industry was the largest consumer of fuel oil, using about 2.5 million tons in 1904, and about 2.1 million tons in 1912. Next in size was railroad consumption, especially in the Volga Embayment. Consumption in 1903 was about 2 million tons, and in 1913 about 1.8 million tons. Heavy demand was also made by navigation, especially in Volga River and Caspian Sea shipping. It used about 1.1 million tons in 1900, and about 820,000 tons in 1910. Industry, railroads, and navigation were the largest consumers of fuel oil, both in processed products of distillation or residue, and in crude oil.

Illuminating oil: The demand for kerosene was high in itself, but low per capita, considering the poor development of the electric power industry, which made petroleum the most important illuminant.

Lubricating oil: Lubricating oil is used chiefly in motorized transportation, mining, and other industries. It is not surprising, therefore, that demand for lubricating oil was low at that time, since industry and transportation were poorly developed. Demand was only about 53,000 tons in 1900, and 200,000 tons in 1912. The major portion of the lubricating oil manufactured was exported.

Gasoline: Gasoline, which is the lightest product in oil processing, originally was not used at all. In Russia and other countries it was considered an obnoxious by-product until the development of the Otto motor[4] in the twentieth century. The rise of motor traffic gave gasoline an undreamed-of importance. Since, however, czarist Russia did not have a motor traffic system, there was little use for gasoline.

This situation shows that processing of crude oil, insofar as the Russian market was concerned, was limited chiefly to the manufacture of fuel oil and kerosene. In general, about 80 per cent of the crude oil produced was shipped to refineries. The remaining 20 per cent was used as crude oil by the railroads.

We have exact statistics for the year 1910 which show the quantity of processed and finished products. With some variation these figures may be applied to the other years preceding World War I:

TABLE 6. Survey of Finished Products Made in Russian Refineries in 1910

Total oil production	9,680,000 tons
Oil laid down in refineries	8,230,000
Total finished products	5,620,000
Fuel	3,010,000
Kerosene	1,360,000
Lubricating oil	295,000
Gasoline and/or naphtha	25,000
Other products (asphalts, etc.)	930,000

Transportation Problems and Oil Exports in the Czarist Era

To transport oil czarist Russia had the following facilities: railroads and tank cars, tankers and barges, and the pipeline from Baku to Batumi which was built by the Russian government between 1897 and 1905. A comparison of these various transportation facilities shows that transportation by water was by far the cheapest.

Both crude and refined oil from the Caucasian fields had to travel

[4] Translator's note: Nikolaus Otto (1832-1891) made the first four-cycle gas motor (the "Otto Gas Machine") in 1876. This was an internal combustion engine.

to the most important domestic centers of consumption in the interior by the following routes:

1. From Baku (Groznyy, Emba, or Cheleken Island) across the Caspian Sea to Astrakhan and then by way of the Volga River into the interior.

2. From Baku by railroad or pipeline to Batumi on the Black Sea. From there the oil was shipped across the Black Sea, up the Don and Dnieper Rivers, into the interior.

The railroad and pipeline from Baku to Batumi, which were built by the government and operated by the State Trans-Caucasian Railroad agency, should have proved a boon for the transportation of oil to Batumi, since the cost to the government for the transport of a pud (about 35 pounds) of oil from Baku to Batumi was only 1.2 kopeks (about 1 cent). However, the government charged 13 kopeks (about 10 cents) for transport through the pipeline and 15 kopeks (about 12.5 cents) by railroad. This proved a serious handicap to transportation of oil to the Black Sea. This is the reason that in 1904, out of a total production of about 10,809,000 tons, only 1,110,000 tons were sent from Baku to Batumi.

This tariff by the Imperial government strangled exports. Exports were possible only from Baku via Batumi and the Black Sea to destinations in Europe and Asia. But as a result of the excessive transportation charges over that route, the oil from the Caucasus took the cheaper way up the Volga River into the interior. This tendency was further strengthened by the inadequacy of the Russian export facilities. Lacking tankers of her own, Russia depended upon foreign tankers for oil export. Von Knorre is correct in saying, "High cost of transportation from Baku to Batumi is responsible for the decline or stagnation in Russian oil exports, and has contributed to the diversion of products into the interior, where cheaper shipping rates prevail."[5] The negligible ratio of Russian oil exports to total oil production is shown in the following table:

TABLE 7. Comparison of Russian Oil Exports with Oil Production

Year	Exports (thousands of tons)	Total Production (thousands of tons)
1910	859	9,680
1911	854	9,108
1912	837	9,361
1913	948	8,648

[5] op.cit., p. 38.

With average annual production at about 9 million tons, exports fluctuated between 840,000 and 950,000 tons; that is, they were about a tenth of Russian production.

Table 8 compares average annual domestic consumption and exports for 1910-1913.

TABLE 8. Comparison of Domestic Consumption with Exports of Russian Oil Products (Annual Averages for the Years 1910-1913)

Products	Domestic Share (thousands of tons)	Exports (thousands of tons)
Crude and fuel oil	3,934	49
Kerosene	901	426
Lubricating oil	107	246
Gasoline and naphtha	32	98
On-the-spot consumption		
In production	1,312	......
In processing	574	......
Other products	......	50
Total	6,860	869

The whole complex of transportation problems is intertwined with inland consumption and oil exports, and can be judged correctly only in connection with these questions.

The End of the Czarist Oil Industry

The comparatively well-developed oil industry of Russia was so severely shaken by the ravages of World War I and subsequent dramatic events that production sank three to four million tons between 1918 and 1921.

The end of the czarist oil industry was especially dramatic at Baku, the center of production, which now became the focus of the international conflict. A decree of the Council of People's Commissars of June 1, 1918 nationalized the entire oil industry, which meant complete expropriation of property without indemnification of the owners. Thereupon the city of Baku and its oil fields were occupied by the Turks in September 1918, and by the English in November of that year. The English favored establishment of an independent, noncommunistic state, Azerbaijan, that would be friendly to the Allies. They rescinded the expropriation of the oil industry and reinstated the former property owners. The transportation of oil into the Russian interior was prevented and prohibited, while export via Batum was promoted in every way. However, the Reds reconquered Baku in May 1920. Again the Soviet government decreed nationalization of the property. Abroad, an early collapse of the Soviet regime, bringing with it recognition of private property rights, was expected. This is the reason why, despite uncertain political and legal situations, a number of people purchased Russian oil shares abroad. The American Standard Oil concern acquired a large block of stock in the Nobel concern, which would have given it control of the Russian petroleum industry if the previous legal status had been restored. A portion of the shares of the Russian General Oil Corporation, including the A. I. Mantashev and G. M. Lianosov groups, was purchased by the Royal Dutch-Shell concern.

American, English, French, and Belgian oil groups formed a bloc in the fall of 1922, and resolved to abstain from concession treaties with the Russian government and any purchase of oil from it until their claims were satisfied. This boycott, however, did not last very long because as early as March 1923 some participants withdrew. A change in the decision of the Soviets could not be forced from the outside. The Soviet oil industry remained socialized and the big oil concerns were excluded from future operation in Russian territory.

This closed the history of the czarist oil industry. In the following three decades there arose in the same territory, but under completely changed conditions, the structure of the Soviet oil industry.[6]

THE DEVELOPMENT OF THE SOVIET OIL INDUSTRY

State Authority and the Oil Industry

The main characteristic distinguishing the czarist from the Soviet oil industry is the fact that no longer do individuals or groups of individuals own the oil fields and plants; now the state itself acts as owner and operator. The land with all deposits, the production and refining plants, and the transportation and distribution systems were taken over in the first move of the government, and came to be the "common property of the people."

From then on the state assumed the undertakings that were carried on by independent businessmen. It is the state that determines the

[6] Translator's note: See Louis Fischer, *Oil Imperialism, the International Struggle for Petroleum* (New York, 1926), for additional information about this period.

place, time, method, and extent of the production, refining, transportation, and distribution of petroleum products. The state decides which drilling and production methods will be used, and orders the construction of refineries and means of transportation. The state supplies manpower and regulates working conditions. It furnishes tools and machinery. The state does the financing and fixes the prices of finished products. All the principles laid down as essentials of the state-planned economy in the section entitled "The Russian Economic System" are applied in practice.

The state has reorganized the entire oil industry within the framework of its new responsibilities.[7] The oil fields, with their installations, and the oil plants were merged into trusts (*trest*) which in turn were combined into larger groups (*obyedinyeniye*). The trusts are subordinate to the groups and the groups are under the control of the Federal Ministry of Petroleum Production, which is the highest authority in the Soviet oil industry. There are some exceptions in that certain trusts are under the immediate control of the Ministry. They are trusts in areas where no groups exist, as on Sakhalin Island. The Minister for Petroleum—at present (1951) Mr. Baibakov—is responsible for the whole Soviet petroleum industry.

The Soviet oil industry is divided into the following groups:

1. The Azneft[8] group in Azerbaijan (the Baku region), with the Artemneft, Azizbekovneft, Beriyaneft, Buzovnyneft, Kaganovichneft, Kirovneft, Leninneft, Molotovneft, Ordzhonikidzeneft, and Stalinneft trusts.

2. The Grozneft group in the Groznyy area (the North Caucasus), with the Oktyabrneft, Tashkalaneft, Malgobekneft, and Staragrozneft trusts.

3. The Krasnodarneft group in the Maykop area (the Northwest Caucasus), with the Apsheronneft, Chadysneft, and Chernomorneft trust.

4. The Kuybyshevneft group in the Ural-Volga region, with the Syzranneft, Stavropolneft, and Kinelneft trusts.

5. The Molotovneft group in the Ural-Volga region, with the Krasnokamneft and Severokamneft trusts.

6. The Bashneft group in the Ural-Volga region, with the Ishimbayneft and Tuymazyneft trusts.

---

[7] See Werner Leimbach, *Die Sowjetunion, Natur, Volk und Wirtschaft* (Stuttgart, 1950), p. 328, and *Erdöl-Informationsdienst*, March 15, 1949.
[8] *Neft* means petroleum.

7. The Kazakhstanneft group in the Emba region, with the Embaneft and Aktyubneft trusts.

8. The Sredasneft group in Central Asia, with the Kalininneft trust.

Also, there are the following trusts under the direct control of the Ministry of Petroleum Production:

1. The Gruzneft trust in Georgia.
2. The Dagneft trust in Dagestan.
3. The Ukrneft trust in the Ukraine.
4. The Buguruslanneft trust in the Ural-Volga region.
5. The Turkmenneft trust in Turkmenistan.
6. The Voroshilovneft trust in Central Asia.
7. The Sakhalinneft trust on Sakhalin Island.

Up to now all these groups and trusts have belonged to either the Southern and Western District or the Eastern District. To the Southern and Western District have belonged the Azneft, Grozneft, and Kraznodarneft groups, and the Gruzneft, Dagneft, Ukrneft, and Turkmenneft trusts. To the Eastern District have belonged the Kuybyshevneft, Molotovneft, Bashneft, Kazakhstanneft, and Sredasneft groups and the Buguruslanneft, Voroshilovneft, and Sakhalinneft trusts. The Ukhta-Pechora area lies in neither of these districts, as it is isolated territory, entirely shut off from the outside, where only forced laborers and exiles work.

Oil Geology and Geophysics

The United States is the undisputed leader among the world's petroleum producers in industrial development and scientific research. Soviet Russia has not invented or developed any new methods of exploration, but has willingly adopted new methods as soon as their usefulness has been established.[9]

The most important fields of the science of petroleum are geology and geophysics, two scientific branches which are in steady and direct contact with practical oil economy. The oil geologist is able to recog-

[9] See Leimbach, *op.cit.*, pp. 23ff., and Alexander Sieger, "Die Organisation der geologischen Erkundung und Forschung in der Sowjetunion," *Zeitschrift für Raumforschung*, 1950, No. 6-7, p. 287. Also Adolf Weber, *Marktwirtschaft und Sowjetwirtschaft* (Munich, 1949), p. 259, where he writes, "Large funds have been allotted to the geological exploration of Russia's wide open spaces. Julian Huxley, former director-general of UNESCO, occasionally mentioned the excellence of that research and said, 'In modern geological and soil research the Russians lead the world.' They have in mind in this case, as always, the future application of results to industrial operations. The use of geological research is based on very well-considered plans."

Sedimentary basin

Oil pipe line

Formby▬ **Proved oil or gas field**

Gas pipe line

Refining center, with estimated crude charging capacity (end 1948) of —

100,000 b/d or more........Ploeşti ◉

10,000 to 100,000 b/d.........Sète ▲

2,000 to 10,000 b/d.............Pécs △

under 2,000 b/d................Rome ✕

uncertain........................Kazan'? △

Brest (Planned).....*Refining center under construction*

o.....*Oil-handling port*

0	100	200	300	400	500 MILES

0	100 200 300 400	500 KILOMETERS

NORWAY

SWEDEN

NORTH SEA

DENMARK

BALTIC

Vallo

Nynäshamn

Kvarntorp ✕

Kvarntorp ✕

EIRE

UNITED KINGDOM

Dundee

Edinburgh

Ardrossan

Midlothian

Heysham

Hull

Formby

Ellesmere Port

Llandarcy

Central England

Thames Est.

Cork

Coryton

Portishead

Dunkerque (Planned)

Southampton

Le Havre

Rouen

Seine

Brest (Planned)

St. Nazaire

Loire

Bordeaux

FRANCE

Pau

St. Marcet

Gabian

Sète

Marseille

BELGIUM

Ghent

Antwerp

NETH.

Pernis

Schoonebeek

Emlichheim

Salzbergen

Düsseldorf

Cologne

Rhine

Oppau

Mannheim

Forst

Pechelbronn

Strasbourg

Danube

Hamburg

Hamburg

Heide

Heide

Bremen

Hanover

Hanover

Elbe

Weser

GERMANY

POLAND

Kralupy

Kolín

M. Ostrava

Pardubice

Przebin

Czechowic

CZECHOSLOV.

Hauskau

Misterdorf

Moosbierbaum

Ebensee

AUSTRIA

Vienna

Bratislava

Göding

Gbely

Budapest

HUNGARY

Pécs △

SWITZERLD.

Trecate (Planned)

Villasanta

Milan

Lodi

Ripalta

Cortemaggiore

Parma

Genoa

La Spezia

Leghorn

Florence

Venice

Fiore

Po

Pietramala

Trieste

Fiume

Sisak

Sava

Goilo

Osijek

Brod

YUGOS.

Adriatic Sea

Bari

Devo

Berg

PORTUGAL

Lisbon

Duero

Tagus

SPAIN

Ebro

Pyrenees

Barcelona

Cartagena (Planned)

Rome ✕

Naples

Tramutola

MEDITERRANEAN

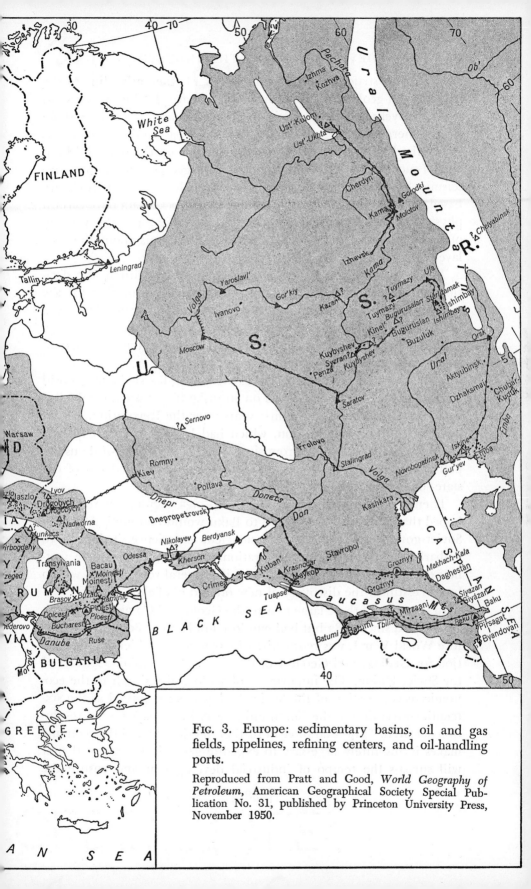

FIG. 3. Europe: sedimentary basins, oil and gas fields, pipelines, refining centers, and oil-handling ports.

Reproduced from Pratt and Good, *World Geography of Petroleum*, American Geographical Society Special Publication No. 31, published by Princeton University Press, November 1950.

nize from the structure of the earth's crust whether, according to the principles of geology, oil could have accumulated in this or that spot. He turns over to the geophysicist, for further examination, only those places where it could have. The geophysicist has a number of working methods at his disposal to get specific data on the type and location of such structures. The most important geophysical methods are seismic, gravitational, electrical, and magnetic. These methods are based on the experience, common to all, that rock strata have certain physical properties—such as gravity, conductivity, and the velocity of elastic waves in them—which permit conclusions about the rock layers.

The findings of the geologist and geophysicist facilitate the decisions of the management as to the most promising location for the test well. Moreover, the oil industry can make long-term plans—e.g., for construction of new refineries and pipelines—because geology and geophysics provide reliable appraisals of the extent and magnitude of oil deposits discovered.

Geologic exploration for oil was carried on in Russia before World War I, but only sporadically and on an insignificant scale. Geological work was also limited in the first years after the Revolution. It centered in the Caspi depression, which had been but little explored and was considered highly promising. The planned, large-scale use of petroleum geology did not begin until 1927, with the advent of the state-controlled economy.

Then the center shifted to the Ural-Volga region, where it was hoped that an oil province equal to Baku would be found. After the Soviet government had gathered sufficient experience, it decided to embark upon a large-scale exploration program geared to the vastness of the country and the wealth of its mineral resources. It was to be successful in the discovery of new oil and gas fields.

In the wake of these large efforts, the Geological Committee, which had existed since 1882 but had employed only 70 or 80 geologists before World War I, was reorganized in 1929 as the Chief Administration for Geology and Geodesy of the Supreme Economic Council of the Soviet Union. The importance of geological research to the economic reconstruction of the Soviet Union was recognized at the sixteenth convention of the Communist party in 1930. A special resolution declared, "The guarantee of further development of the economy makes it absolutely necessary to expedite geological work so that it will surpass the tempo of industrial development and ensure the timely collection of a supply of mineral raw materials." The Chief Administration for Geology and Geodesy of the Supreme Economic Council of the Soviet Union became, by decree of June 14, 1946, the Ministry of Geology, with the task of coordinating all geological work for the discovery and recovery of the rich mineral resources of the Soviet Union. This concentration, with a supreme state authority at the top, meant a compact centralization of the entire geological service and an intensification of geological prospecting and exploration, including a complete geological survey of the country. This supreme authority controls the geological agencies and the local and central scientific institutes devoted to related work. Thus there is attached to the Academy of Sciences a geological-geographical department. Also, there should be mentioned the Institute for Geological Sciences, Institute for Petroleum Geology, Geological Museum, and Institute for Theoretical Geophysics. They perform the scientific and political tasks assigned to them by the government and fulfill the practical needs of the Russian oil industry.

On account of the planned cooperation of the state, the economy, and science, three quarters of the entire area of the Soviet Union had been geologically explored up to 1947.

TABLE 9. Geological Prospecting of Russian Territory

From	To	Per Cent of Russian Territory Prospected
	1918	10.5
1919	1929	7.5
1930	1934	17.8
1935	1938	29.2
1939	1940	0.8
1941	1945	7.0
1946	1947	2.2
Total		75.0

In geophysical prospecting the Soviet Union applied the generally known and proved methods of gravitational, electrical, magnetic, and seismic measurement, and in addition it used the method of gas measurement.[10]

1. The gravitational method, employing pendulum and torsion balance, has taken the gravity of rocks as a starting point for its

[10] Translator's note: The translation of the following outline is based upon L. L. Nettleton's *Geophysical Prospecting for Oil* (New York, 1940), p. 444.

calculations. The Soviet Union used this method for the first time in 1933 when a large-scale general gravitational survey was decreed. The first systematic and detailed work was carried out in the Emba region, where many salt domes, so important in oil exploration, were found with the help of torsion balance.

2. The electrical method, used mainly for measurements near the surface, is based upon the knowledge that strata of rocks vary in, and can be identified through, conductivity. These electrical-resistance methods were first used in 1929 in Groznyy, where about 5,000 square miles have been surveyed. This method was soon to play an important role in the exploration of the Soviet Union.

3. The magnetic method uses the magnetic properties of rocks as means of identification. This method was at first little employed in the Soviet Union. It had been applied before World War I when the Kursker anomaly was surveyed, but in 1930 only one party was using this method. Even after 1935 there were not more than nine crews taking magnetic measurements.

4. The seismic method, which is of the greatest importance in prospecting for oil, depends upon the study of artificially produced waves, which are measured by highly sensitive seismographs. The measurement of the travel time of these waves permits determination of the position of rock strata. Development of this method in the Soviet Union was comparatively slow until it was possible to use it in a large territory. Reflection and refraction measurements were first made in 1933 in the Emba region and in some areas of West Asia. From 1934 on, measurements were made in Baku, in the shallow coastal waters of the Caspian Sea, and in the vast spaces of the Second Baku, especially at Ishimbay.

5. In addition to these widely used methods, there is the so-called gas-measurement method, used more in the Soviet Union than elsewhere. In this procedure samples of soil are taken to a depth of two to six meters and tested for their methane and, particularly, their heavy hydrocarbon content. From the gas content and composition thus established can be drawn conclusions as to the occurrence of oil and gas deposits. This method, with its shortcomings, is rather crude. It does not provide reliable information on the deeper beds, which are important in the recovery of oil. However, Russian literature emphasizes that this method has achieved results above all others in

the Maykop area, where it has been applied consistently since 1935.

The following table shows the number of geophysical crews employed during the first ten years of the state-planned economy:

TABLE 10. Number of Geophysical Crews Used in Exploration

Method	1925	1927	1928	1929	1930	1931	1932	1933	1934	1935
1. Gravitational method	2	3	6	9	11	12	16	17	17	21
2. Electrical method	....	....	....	2	6	9	13	17	29	40
3. Magnetic method	....	....	....	....	1	5	6	8	8	9
4. Seismic method	....	....	....	3	2	1	3	4	5	9
5. Gas-measurement method	....	....	....	....	....	....	....	5	12	19
Total	2	3	6	14	20	27	38	51	71	98

Even though the number of crews employed in prospecting petroliferous areas cannot be taken as a yardstick for evaluation of the geophysical work, it still gives an idea of the gradual increase in scientific effort in the wake of the first and second Five-Year Plans. While there were only two crews in 1926, there were in 1935 almost 100 geophysical parties. It is interesting to note that about half of these parties operated in the Ural-Volga area. During the third Five-Year Plan, which was primarily devoted to the recovery of oil, coal, and metal deposits, systematic exploration began on a large scale, and was not limited to the European districts but extended to the Asiatic areas as well.

Geophysical work was interrupted during World War II in the battle zones (the Carpathians, the Ukraine, the Caucasus). However, in other portions of the country—the Ukhta-Pechora region, the Ural-Volga region, and Central Asia—this work was greatly intensified because of the increased demand for oil in the war. After the war work was resumed throughout the entire country.

The geological and geophysical work done so far proves that Soviet petroleum science is far from reaching the limits of its possibilities. The gigantic size of the Soviet Union means that decades of work will be required before the entire area has been completely explored, and all hidden oil deposits recognized and outlined. According to Soviet reports, more than 1,000 geological-geophysical prospecting parties, equipped with modern instruments, are working today in the exploration of mineral resources in the central and peripheral parts of the Union. The oil industry will also profit from this scientific work.[11]

Drilling and Production Techniques

It has been said above that the Soviet Union adopted readily the geological and geophysical methods of the Western world, but this is true only with certain limitations with regard to drilling and production techniques. In petroleum technology the Russians were not only apt pupils but accomplished remarkable achievements of their own. They had depended for many years on the import of technical equipment from the United States and the other highly developed industrial countries of the West. They now began to make great efforts to become independent of the technical tutelage of the West in drilling and production techniques, and also in transportation and refining.

Efficiency in oil production depends largely on the status of drilling techniques. In the United States serious attention has always been paid to the improvement of drilling methods and equipment. The great success of the United States and its distinct advantage over all other oil countries are not due least to technical perfection in the construction of improved mobile derricks and precise drilling bits, the standardization of tools, and the vastly improved adequacy of flushing fluids. Russian production could only follow slowly the rapid rise of American oil production, primarily on account of the lack of a modern, efficient drilling technique.

The introduction of rotary drilling ushered in a new epoch in the oil industry. This method was developed in the United States after the beginning of this century and was introduced into the Soviet Union following World War I. The results achieved with rotary drilling in the Soviet Union today are not far behind the drilling results of the American oil companies. The world's deepest well has been drilled in Wyoming, in the United States, to a depth of 20,551 feet. Early in 1950 some wells in the Soviet Union were drilled to depths in excess of 16,700 feet; for example, in the trust of Ordzhonikidzeneft in the Baku region.[12] Depth generally does not indicate a

---

[11] Translator's note: See *Geochemical and Mineralogical Methods of Prospecting for Mineral Deposits*, translated from the Russian by Lydia Hartstock and A. Pierce (U.S. Geological Survey Circular No. 127 [Washington, D.C., 1952]), free on application to the Geological Survey, Washington 25, D.C. Originally published by the All-Union Academy of Science, Moscow.

[12] See *Erdöl und Kohle*, III (1950), 99.

high degree of drilling skill, because geological conditions, as well as drilling conditions, play a most important part. Nevertheless, such accomplishments seem to be of importance in judging Soviet drilling technique. In most cases Soviet drilling reached only comparatively shallow depths until the Second World War. The deepest wells in the Baku region reached 8,400 feet in 1939. In the other Caucasian areas and Turkmenistan the deepest wells were 6,700 feet. Outside these areas the deepest wells were not more than 2,600 feet. During World War II some wells in the Second Baku fields reached 10,800 feet, e.g., in Tuymazy. However, the average depth of Russian wells was then but 2,000 to 2,300 feet. The fourth Five-Year Plan endeavored to increase the average depth of the wells in the Second Baku region from 5,700 to 6,560 feet.[13]

Drilling efficiency is measured by drilling time in addition to depth reached. In this regard, also, the Soviets made great progress. In czarist times it sometimes took two years to drill a hole to a few hundred meters in the Baku fields. In April 1949, in the new Buzovny field in Baku, the average performance of drilling equipment was about 8,300 feet a month. It is reported that one drilling outfit established a record of 13,300 feet in one month.[14] This instance could have been the result of favorable geological structure which generally cannot be found. However, the progress in Soviet drilling is evident. Of 3,260 rotary drilling rigs in use in all the oil countries of the world in 1949, the Soviet Union with her satellites had about 600, while Western Germany operated 80, Canada about 90, and the United States 2,140.[15]

Also, underwater drilling, first used in the coastal waters of the Gulf of Mexico and off California, meanwhile had been launched in the Soviet Union. Exploitation of oil deposits off Baku, which continues under the surface of the Caspian Sea, has been energetically and successfully carried on during the past few years.[16] In the shallow sea off Baku, particularly in the bay of Bibi-Eybat, artificial islands similar to those used in the United States have been built, and drilling rigs installed. In 1950, 20 submarine wells were being drilled off Baku.[17]

[13] See "Is Petroleum a Soviet Weakness?" by D. B. Shimkin in the *Oil and Gas Journal*, December 21, 1950, pp. 217-218.
[14] See *Erdöl-Informationsdienst*, September 15, 1949.
[15] See *Erdöl und Kohle*, III (1950), 357.   [16] See *ibid.*, p. 99.
[17] Translator's note: According to latest reports, underwater drilling in the Bay of Baku is reaching considerable proportions. Depths vary between about 10,000 and 13,000

A Soviet method which is not limited to the Soviet Union is the so-called turbine drilling method, which is supposed to have been developed by the Russian engineer Kapeljushnikov. In this method the bit is propelled by built-in turbines, located directly above the bottom of the hole, and not by motors. The advantage of this method over the rotary method is that the drill stem does not rotate with the bit. Drilling by this method, supplemented by directional drilling, in which six to eight holes can be drilled by deflection from a single drilling, has been introduced on a larger scale during the third Five-Year Plan.[18]

TABLE 11. Russian Drilling Performance and Increase in Production

Year	Footage Drilled (thousands of feet)	Production (thousands of tons)
1925	580	7,280
1928	980	11,663
1930	2,133	17,280
1931	2,343	22,412
1932	2,483	21,245
1933	2,787	21,310
1934	4,187	24,063

Since the proved oil deposits become depleted during production, production can be maintained only if new oil fields are constantly discovered and developed. There is a close connection between the amount of production and meters drilled. In Germany, to maintain present production, it is necessary to drill one and one-third inches for exploration and one and one-half inches for development, a total of about three inches, for each ton of oil produced. However, in 1941 the United States, with a total production of 190 million tons, drilled about 100 million feet, and in 1948, with a total production of 207 million tons, drilled about 140 million feet. There the average drilling depth was only one and one-quarter inches per ton of oil produced. For Russia the average drilling depth is two inches per ton, which lies between the German and American figures. Thus it was necessary to drill about 33 million feet in 1950 to produce 37.6 mil-

---

feet. Dozens of steel barges have been moved out into the open sea, and workers live on the barges or on special ships to avoid loss of time in taking them ashore and back to the barges.

[18] Translator's note: See *Petroleum Press Service*, March 1952, p. 98.

lion tons. This must be accomplished each year by the Soviet Union if production at the present level is to be maintained.

In addition to drilling techniques, production techniques have been improved considerably through application of secondary recovery methods. Recovery of oil deposits by means of the primary methods of flow, bailing, pumping and amounts usually to as much as 30 per cent of the oil and sometimes to as much as 40 per cent. The use of secondary recovery methods—water flooding or injection of gas or air into the reservoir—permits production of up to 70 per cent of the oil in place. Increase in oil production depends not alone on increased drilling footage. Just as important is the application of refined production methods, which makes possible an almost complete recovery of the oil in place.

Secondary recovery methods are known of course to Soviet petroleum engineers also, but they did not use them prior to 1944. Soviet publications mention again and again that "secret new secondary recovery methods are used" which make possible the resumption of operation of abandoned wells. Therefore, the publications refer in these cases to the methods of gas or water flooding or air pressuring used by other countries. The use of these methods is limited to certain areas. As far as could be ascertained they have been employed only in the Caucasian region, the Emba district, and in the oil fields of the Second Baku, especially at Tuymazy and Krasnokamsk.[19]

Since the Soviet Union has recognized the importance of improved production methods for more conservative exploitation of the oil deposits, it promulgated the decree of January 1, 1941, which permits exploitation of oil deposits only if control and use of the natural gas which flows out with the oil is guaranteed.

Oil Production and Refining

When the Soviet government took over the Russian oil industry, in a time of internal and external unrest, production had reached its lowest level in many years—3.7 million tons. For four years, from 1918 through 1921, it continued at this low level. With the realization in 1922 of the NEP policy promulgated by Lenin, the Russian oil industry began to recover. The positive effects of this new policy could be observed in all fields of Russian economy, including the oil industry. From 1922 to 1927—that is, from the beginning to the end of the NEP period—oil production increased from 4.9 to 10.6 million

19 See Shimkin, *op.cit.*, p. 218.

tons. Ten years after the Revolution the Russian oil industry produced the same quantity of oil as it had produced at the turn of the century, when Russia for a short time was first of all the oil-producing countries of the world. While the Soviet Union only succeeded in attaining the production of 1900 with the greatest effort, world oil production meanwhile had grown almost ninefold. It had risen from 20.5 million tons in 1900 to about 174 million tons in 1927.

With the start of the state-planned economy, a systematic expansion of the Soviet oil industry also began. From 1928 until World War II Soviet production showed a constantly rising trend.

During the first Five-Year Plan, 1928-1932, 1.6 billion rubles were invested in the oil industry. The technical equipment in the fields was improved, new pipelines were constructed, exports were promoted, and drilling footage was increased. These efforts were not without success. In the five years of the first Plan oil production rose from 11.8 million tons (in 1928) to 21.6 million tons (in 1932).

The second Five-Year Plan, 1933-1937, allotted the oil industry 2.5 billion rubles and concentrated essentially on two things: construction of new refineries and cracking plants, and development of new oil fields in the Ural-Volga area. A comparison of scheduled with actual production shows that potential production had been greatly overestimated.

TABLE 12. Scheduled and Actual Production Figures for the Second Five-Year Plan, 1933-1937

Year	Planned Production (millions of tons)	Actual Production (millions of tons)
1933	29.5	21.6
1934	34.5	24.5
1935	42.4	25.5
1936	52.6	26.1
1937	68.1	27.1

The third Five-Year Plan, 1938-1942, interrupted by the war, emphasized further development of the Ural-Volga region, the oil fields of which were to be connected by a far-flung pipeline system with the industrial areas of the Urals and Central Russia. Also planned were construction of refineries, increased use of rotary drilling, and especially the geological and geophysical exploration of Central Asia and Siberia. In 1938, the first year of this plan, production was 28.2 million tons as shown by producing areas in the following table:

TABLE 13. Oil Production of the Russian Oil Areas in 1938

Area	Actual Production (millions of tons)	Percentage of Total Production
Baku (including Georgia)	20.7	73.4
Groznyy	2.3	8.1
Maykop	2.0	7.1
Dagestan	0.2	0.7
Emba	0.5	1.8
Ural-Volga region	1.6	5.6
Central Asia	0.3	1.1
Sakhalin	0.3	1.1
Turkmenistan	0.2	0.7
Ukhta-Pechora	0.1	0.4
Total	28.2	100.0

At the conclusion of the third Five-Year Plan in 1942 a total production of 47.4 million tons was scheduled as follows, with Turkmenistan and Ukhta-Pechora excluded:

TABLE 14. Oil Production Scheduled for 1942

Area	Scheduled Production (millions of tons)	Percentage of Total Production
Baku (including Georgia)	27.0	57.0
Groznyy	4.1	8.6
Maykop	3.7	7.8
Dagestan	0.6	1.3
Emba	2.0	4.2
Ural-Volga region	7.0	14.7
Central Asia	1.7	3.7
Sakhalin	1.3	2.7
Total	47.4	100.0

Actually only 31.8 million tons instead of the requested 47.4 million tons were produced in 1942.[20] The high expectations of the Soviet government for the development of oil production did not come true.

The Second World War hit the oil industry hard, particularly between 1942 and 1945, but from 1947 on the decline of the industry was brought to a stop.

The fourth Five-Year Plan, 1946-1950, was announced in March 1946 and envisioned an increase in annual oil production to 35.4

[20] According to Shimkin, op.cit., oil production was only 18 million tons in 1942.

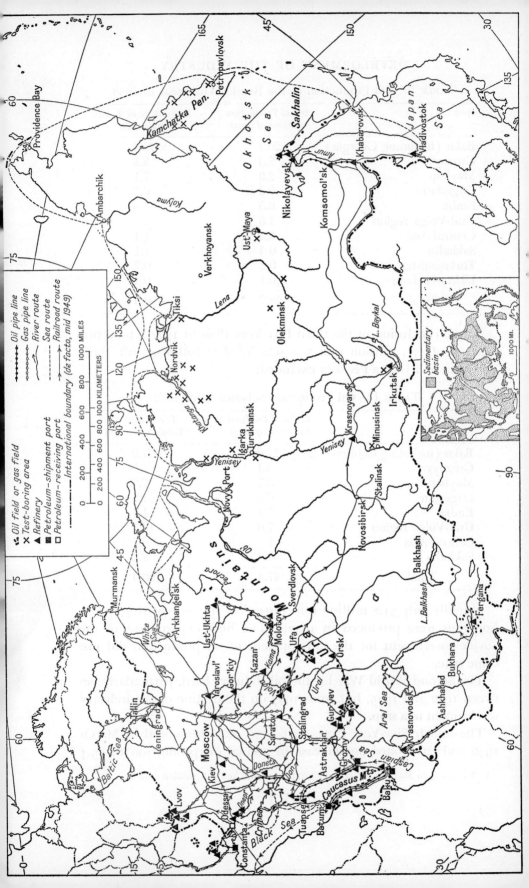

million tons. In contrast to the overly high figures scheduled for the last years of the second and third Five-Year Plans, 68.1 and 47.4 million tons respectively, this demand for 35.4 million tons was based upon a realistic estimate of actual Russian oil potentialities.

The scheduled figures of the fourth Five-Year Plan are shown in Table 15 by individual Soviet republics and not by oil regions:

TABLE 15. Oil Production Scheduled for 1950

Soviet Republic	Scheduled Production (thousands of tons)	Percentage of Total Production
Azerbaijan SSR (Baku region)	17,000	47.9
Russian SFSR (Groznyy, Maykop, Dagestan, Molotov, Ufa, Kuybyshev, Ukhta-Pechora, and Sakhalin regions)	14,500	40.9
Kazakh SSR (Emba region)	1,200	3.4
Turkmen SSR (Turkmenistan area)	1,100	3.1
Uzbek SSR (Central Asian area)	1,066	3.1
Ukrainian SSR (district of the Western and Central Ukraine)	325	0.9
Georgian SSR (Georgian area)	110	0.3
Kirghiz SSR	80	0.2
Tadzhik SSR	60	0.2
Total	35,441	100.0

These figures of the Plan were exceeded in a production of 37.6 million tons.[21] Although it is not possible to give absolutely correct figures for the several producing areas, it can reasonably be assumed that the figures in Table 16 approach reality.

In arranging these production results according to the usual divisions—i.e., the southern and western oil districts (Baku, Groznyy, Maykop, Dagestan, Georgia, Turkmenistan, and the Ukraine) and the eastern districts (Molotov, Ufa, Kuybyshev, Ukhta-Pechora, Emba, Central Asia, and Sakhalin)—it is found that in 1950 the first group produced 59.8 per cent of the total (about 22.5 million tons) while the last group yielded only 40.2 per cent (about 15.1 million tons).[22]

[21] Press reports such as that in *Main-Post* (Würzburg), March 5, 1951—"It has been proved that the goal of the Five-Year Plan, which was to provide Russia with a production of more than 35 million tons, has by no means been reached in 1950"—do not represent the facts.

[22] These figures refute a number of incorrect statements heard over and over again about Soviet oil production and policy. It is not true that the southern and western regions fell behind the eastern regions in oil production. The opinion voiced in the

TABLE 16. Oil Production in 1950

Area	Production (thousands of tons)	Percentage of Total Production
Baku	17,000	45.2
Groznyy	1,800	4.8
Maykop	1,500	4.0
Dagestan	500	1.3
Georgia	120	0.3
Turkmenistan	1,250	3.3
The Ukraine	330	0.9
Second Baku (Molotov, Ufa, Kuybyshev)	10,600	28.2
Emba	1,300	3.5
Ukhta-Pechora	800	2.1
Central Asia (Fergana Valley)	1,200	3.2
Sakhalin	1,200	3.2
Total	37,600	100.0

article "Russia's Oil," *Mining Journal*, March 9, 1951, that the southern and western districts had produced only about 16.6 million tons but the eastern districts 20.8 million tons is not correct. This article contrasts the southern and western areas with the central areas (Molotov, Ufa, Kuybyshev, Ukhta-Pechora, and Emba), and also with the eastern districts (Fergana and Sakhalin), and says: "A notable change in the oil picture is the marked decline in the production in *the western and southern regions*. As far as one's interpretation of Russian published figures allow, it would appear that total output last year from these regions was only 16,600,000 tons, falling far short of planned figures of 22,700,000 tons. This deficiency has, however, been more than made good by the growth of production in other regions, where total output last year appears to have been 21,000,000 tons against a planned figure of 12,700,000 tons.

"The *central region* is now the most important oil region in the USSR. It covers the Second Baku in the Ural-Volga basin, the old-established producing area at Emba to the north of the Caspian Sea, and the Pechora district in the European Far North, where output has now started, and which, in view of the new strategic importance of the Arctic region, may be of great potential value. The total output of the central region has risen from less than 3,000,000 tons in 1940 to about 18,800,000 tons, and now represents half the total output of the Union.

The *Eastern region* contains only two producing areas of any importance, each of them with an output of about 1,000,000 tons annually—the one at Fergana in Turkestan, north of Afghanistan, the other in Sakhalin."

The claim that the strategically vulnerable oil districts in the Caucasus no longer have a dominant position in the Russian oil industry and that Baku is being neglected intentionally (see recurring articles such as "Ölstrategie entthront Baku") are false. On the other hand, those reports are wrong which deny that the Second Baku and the eastern districts have gained great importance. According to a report in the magazine *Der Volkswirt*, March 2, 1951, P. F. Hellin said in a lecture to the Society of Political Economy in 1947, "The oil fields of the Caucasus because of their exposure to air attack, are so vulnerable that the preponderance of the Western Hemisphere will make itself felt soon. The other oil deposits in the East, the Urals, Lake Baikal, and South Sakhalin have hardly any significance," an opinion which, if it was voiced in this form, is clearly refuted by the statistics in Table 16.

Finally, Anton Zischka in his book, *Asien, Hoffnung einer neuen Welt* (Oldenburg, 1950), p. 189, is incorrect when he says that "Siberia has produced 7 million tons of oil in 1940." This is absolutely wrong.

This production comes from 18,000 to 20,000 oil wells. The number of producing wells does not mean much in evaluating an oil region, since productivity of the wells varies greatly. In the United States in 1950, approximately 450,000 wells produced about 270 million tons. In the Middle East, however, only about 200 wells produced 86 million tons in 1950. These two figures show how careful one should be in comparing several oil regions, if the number of producing wells is made a yardstick. The number of producing wells is a significant factor in the evaluation of oil districts only if geological conditions are similar. The Soviet Union operated in 1934 about 6,000 wells, and added an average of 1,500 wells annually. As a result, at the beginning of the Russo-German War in 1941 about 15,000 wells were producing.[23] During the war years 2,500 new wells were drilled, a number just sufficient to replace the wells depleted during four years of war. The fourth Five-Year Plan demanded for 1946 through 1950 the drilling of 5,500 additional wells, of which 3,500 were to be drilled in the Second Baku. With approximately 19,000 producing wells in 1950, annual production was about 2,000 tons, and daily production about 5.5 tons, per well.

For 1960 Stalin demanded oil production of 60 million tons, in addition to coal production of 500 million tons, pig iron production of 50 million tons, and steel production of 60 million tons. Soviet experts are convinced that the fifth Five-Year Plan, 1951-1955, will reach Stalin's figures.[24]

Refining capacity: The rank of an oil industry is determined not only by its productive capacity; also of great significance is its refining capacity. The oil cannot be used in the condition in which it is produced; rather complicated chemical and physical processing methods are necessary to obtain the finished products required by a modern economy.

The refineries taken over from the czarist industry by the Soviets were partly obsolete and partly useless on account of the effects of the war and the revolution. Only with the beginning of the planned economy was construction of modern processing plants begun. During the first Five-Year Plan refinery equipment was acquired from abroad, especially from the United States. Increase in refining capacity was emphasized, especially in the second Five-Year Plan. During that pe-

[23] See Shimkin, *op.cit.*, p. 217.
[24] Translator's note: It is generally believed that the target of 60 million metric tons of oil annually may be reached by 1955. See also *Petroleum Press Service, op.cit.*, p. 97.

riod refineries with an annual throughput of 7.7 million tons were built. At the beginning of the third Five-Year Plan more than three quarters of the total refining capacity, about 77 per cent, was located in the Baku region, 12 per cent at Groznyy (which also refined oil from Baku, because the deposits at Groznyy were considerably over-estimated), and 5 per cent in the Maykop area. Toward the end of the third Five-Year Plan, refining capacity was expanded considerably. With the development of the Second Baku, the Caucasian region lost its outstanding position. Modern refineries were constructed in Saratov, Syzran, Sterlitamak, Ishimbay, Tuymazy, Molotov, and Buguruslan. Moreover, refineries were built or existing plants enlarged not only in production centers but also in consumption centers; for instance, in Rostov, Stalingrad, Moscow, and Leningrad.

Cracking capacity: With total refining capacity, cracking capacity plays an important role in the Soviet Union,[25] because the Russian crude oils, with the exception of the northern Caucasian oils, yield but little gasoline (between 5 and 10 per cent) by the older methods of distillation and refining. It was necessary for the Russian petroleum economy to have at its disposal sufficient cracking capacity to increase the yield of gasoline. The Soviet authorities began in 1928 to build cracking plants. In 1937 cracking capacity was said to be 9.25 million tons. Production from these plants was reported as follows:

Gasoline	1,750,000 tons
Kerosene	1,500,000 tons
Motor and diesel fuels	325,000 tons

Refining output from 1925 to 1938 is shown in Table 17.

Most of these plants are combinations of refining and cracking installations, and are located in the more important oil-producing districts: Baku, Groznyy, and the Second Baku. But large plants are located in the oil-consuming centers. The following list gives the location of the most important refineries in the Soviet Union.

Location of the Major Soviet Refineries

Andizhan	Chelyabinsk	Gorodki	Ishimbay
Baku	Drogobych	Groznyy	Iskininskiy
Batumi	Fergana	Guryev	Kanibadam
Buguruslan	Gorki	Irkutsk	Kazan

25 See Shimkin, *op.cit.*, p. 224.

Khabarovsk	Makhachkala	Novobogatinskoye	Syzran
Kherson	Melnikovo	Odessa	Tbilisi
Komsomolsk	Mirzaani	Oka	Tuapse
Krasnodar	Molotov	Orsk	Tuymazy
Krasnovodsk	Moscow	Osipenko	Ufa
Krasnoyarsk	Moskalvo	Saratov	Ukhta
Kuybyshev	Nadvornaya	Stalingrad	Vladivostok
Leningrad	Nebit-Dag	Sterlitamak	Yaroslavl
Leninsk	Nikolayev	Stry	
Lvov	Nikolayevsk	Strzelbice	

TABLE 17. Crude Oil Processed in Russian Refineries[26]

Budget or Calendar Year	Processed Crude Oil (millions of tons)
1925/26	5.8
1926/27	7.0
1927/28	8.7
1928/29	12.0
1929/30	14.8
1930	16.2
1931	19.9
1932	20.2
1933	18.5
1934	20.8
1935	20.9
1936	22.6
1937	25.7
1938	28.4

Several locations have more than one refinery: for instance, Baku has five;[26a] Drogobych and Fergana, four each; Groznyy, three; and Molotov, two. In 1951 the Soviet Union had at least 66 such oil-processing plants, differing very considerably, of course, in size and capacity. The total refining capacity of all these plants is between 33 and 35 million tons. The cracking capacity is between 13 and 14 million tons.[27]

26 See W. Doellen in *Öl und Kohle*, xxxvii (1941), 744.

26a Translator's note: In the Baku area are six major refineries and many pipelines.

27 See Dr. Gustav Egloff's address, "Strategic Oil Supplies," presented at the convention of the American Petroleum Institute in Los Angeles on November 14, 1950. (Translator's note: For Dr. Egloff's address, see the *Petroleum Engineer*, Reference Annual, 1951.) Dr. Egloff estimated that the throughput of the Soviet refineries at the end of 1949 was 680,000 barrels a day, making the annual capacity 35 million tons. Also see Shimkin, *op.cit.* Shimkin says that "Soviet national cracking capacity today approxi-

Oil Exports and Domestic Consumption

The consumption of oil is a sure indication of the technical level of a nation. The demand for gasoline and diesel fuels and lubricants is highly indicative of the capacity of its industry and the intensity of its transportation. In czarist times oil consumption was comparatively small, limited essentially to fuel oil and kerosene. This clearly reflected the poor technical development of that economy. In the Soviet era, demand for oil at first was insignificant. Thus, with increased oil production, a larger quantity was available for export from 1923 on. Until 1932 exports increased consistently. But with the second Five-Year Plan a decisive change occurred. The promotion of industrialization, motorization, and mechanization increased domestic demand and resulted in the limitation of oil exports. These countercurrents, the development of oil exports on the one side and of domestic consumption on the other, came to a climax. As a result, exports have practically ceased, while domestic consumption can hardly be covered by domestic production.

Oil exports: Oil exports, which had reached almost a million tons before World War I, were reduced to practically nothing in the first years after the October Revolution because of the decline in oil production. In 1921-1922 they were only 140,000 tons. From 1923 on exports increased year by year. They were about 3.5 million tons in 1930

---

mates 17.5-18 million metric tons (127-131 million barrels)." He points out that during World War II the Soviet Union obtained, under lend-lease, three cracking plants, with an annual capacity of about three million tons, which were erected in Kuybyshev, Ufa, and Orsk. Nonetheless, the estimate of Russian cracking capacity as 17 to 18 million tons seems too high. The present author thinks that it is at present no more than 14 million tons. Also see *Erdöl und Kohle*, III (1950), 253 and 638.

Translator's note: See *Petroleum Press Service, op.cit.*, p. 98: "Mr. Baibakov, the Minister for the Oil Industry, stated that new trunk pipelines both for oil and gas, were completed last year; and . . . that refineries were completed in 1951 with a throughput capacity of six million barrels annually. Refinery yields and the quality of finished products are stated to have been improved. Gasoline production last year (1951) rose by 20 per cent, diesel oil production by 45 per cent, and kerosene production by 3 per cent." According to *Erdöl und Kohle*, V (1952), 265, Kalamkarov, Soviet deputy minister for the oil industry, declared that construction of new refineries and growth of throughput capacity are to be accelerated. Output of high-grade oil products is to be increased and, at the same time, losses of crude oil in the refining process are to be kept as low as possible. Shortcomings experienced in some refineries are to be eliminated and production targets fulfilled. Also see Dahl M. Duff, "Refining in Russia," the *Oil and Gas Journal*, March 17, 1952, p. 181. He points out the deficiencies of the Russian petroleum industry, and also certain advantages it holds over its counterpart in the Western world. Finally, see M. N. Jurin, "Can Russia Produce 600 M. Bbls. of Oil Annually by 1955?" *World Oil*, March 1953, pp. 236ff.; and D. B. Shimkin, *Minerals—A Key to Soviet Power* (Cambridge, Mass., 1953).

and reached 5.2 million in 1931. In 1932 exports exceeded 6 million tons. This was a peak in the development of Russian oil exports; oil took second place in all Russian foreign trade only to lumber. Foreign-exchange receipts from these exports were used to finance importation of machinery and technical equipment, which were needed to carry out extensive projected industrialization.[28] The chief countries to which Russian oil flowed at this time were Italy, France, Germany, England, Belgium, Spain, Sweden, and Denmark.

The appearance of such large quantities of Russian oil on the world market challenged the Anglo-American oil companies, which were forced to defend themselves against the cheap Russian oil. During the 1930's violent price wars ensued from Russia's pursuance of its oil export policy.

With industrialization and motorization progressing, oil exports declined. In 1933 they were again below five million tons. In 1938 they were less than one million tons. Since the Second World War they have ceased entirely, except in extraordinary circumstances such as those which brought about the delivery of large quantities to China and to Korea. *At present* Russian oil is no threat to other oil countries. However, it could become a danger again some day if the Soviet government should shatter the international price structure with a deliberate dumping of even small quantities.

TABLE 18. Development of Russian Oil Exports in the Decisive Years from 1921 through 1938

Budget Year	Exports (thousands of tons)	Calendar Year	Exports (thousands of tons)
1921/22	140	1930	3,459
1922/23	309	1931	5,212
1923/24	723	1932	6,106
1924/25	1,337	1933	4,890
1925/26	1,474	1934	4,310
1926/27	2,039	1935	3,354
1927/28	2,784	1936	2,660
1928/29	3,620	1937	1,930
1929/30	2,716	1938	931

[28] See A. Weber, *Marktwirtschaft und Sowjetwirtschaft, op.cit.,* p. 342. There the author quotes a statement from a paper published in 1946 by Ohio State University: "The Soviet Union was forced to dispose of her commodities for export at any price to pay for imports that were absolutely necessary to carry out the first Four [*sic*]-Year Plan."

With the decline of oil exports from year to year domestic consumption increased more and more. In 1913 Russian domestic consumption of oil products was 6.8 million tons. Demand was at the same level at the beginning of the first Five-Year Plan (1928). But between 1929 to 1939 consumption tripled, reaching about 23 million tons. Table 19 shows the development of Russian oil consumption between 1929 and 1939.

TABLE 19. Development of Russian Oil Consumption
from 1929 to 1939[29]
(excluding consumption in the fields and refineries)

Year	Consumption of Oil Products (millions of tons)
1929	7.8
1930	10.6
1931	12.5
1932	14.3
1933	13.8
1934	15.5
1935	17.2
1936	19.0
1937	23.0
1938	23.0
1939	23.0

In the main, Soviet domestic consumption is determined by the demands of the five most important consumers: industry, transportation, agriculture, homes, and the Soviet armed forces.

Industry: With increasing industrialization of the Soviet Union the demand for oil products throughout industry was increased. Consumption of lubricants occupied first place, as indispensable for all machinery and motors, mobile or stationary. Consider that between 1913 and 1950 coal production rose from 29 to 261 million tons, pig iron production from 4.2 to 19.5 million tons, and steel production from 4.2 to 7 million tons, and that the rest of industry also developed rapidly, and you get an idea of the increase in the use of lubricants which followed such industrialization. At the same tempo grew the demand for fuel oil, which in industry is mainly used by the combustion engines of power plants. Power plants with combustion engines designed exclusively for the use of fuel oil are found only in

[29] From *Moniteur du Pétrole Roumain* (1940), p. 1222.

Baku. However, fuel oil is used also as a source of energy in the power plants of the Central Russian industrial district and the industrial district of Leningrad. There the power plants are adjusted as a rule to the use of mixed fuels and oil is preferred which is subject to easy transportation and has high caloric content.[30] Power plants driven by combustion engines share proportionately the credit for the increase of the production of energy from Russian power plants, the capacity of which grew from 1.1 million kilowatts in 1913 to 20.4 million kilowatts in 1950. Production in the same years rose from 2 billion kilowatt-hours to about 82 billion kilowatt-hours. Of a total consumption of 13.3 million tons of fuels and lubricants in 1937, 6 million tons were consumed by industry.[31]

Transportation: Transportation plays a most important part in a country as vast as the Soviet Union. The most important of all types of transportation in the Soviet Union are railroads and inland navigation, followed by motor traffic and air traffic. Ocean shipping is negligible. In July 1950 the Soviet merchant marine accounted for 2,130,000 gross registered tons out of total world tonnage of 84,580,-000 gross registered tons.[32]

The railroad system of the Soviet Union has been substantially enlarged during the Five-Year Plans. In 1947 it had a length of about 70,000 miles, compared with 38,000 miles in 1913.[33] The waterways in the Union totalled about 66,000 miles in 1938. Inland shipping carried 67 million tons of freight at that time, including 9.6 million tons of oil. Since then, the waterway system has been tremendously improved by regulation of rivers and construction of canals. Motor traffic in the Soviet Union cannot be compared with the extremely rapid motorization in the United States and other highly civilized countries of the West. However, its development is remarkable. The Soviet Union manufactured 1,400 automobiles in 1929, 50,000 in 1933, and in excess of 200,000 in 1938. Production of automobiles in 1950 is reported to have been about half a million. Like automobile traffic, air traffic was stepped up. The Russian airway system for freight and passenger traffic covered about 52,000 miles in 1950. Its

[30] See Erich Thiel, "Die Elektrifizierung der Sowjetunion," *Zeitschrift für Raumforschung*, 1950, No. 3-5, p. 178.

[31] See Shimkin, *op.cit.*, p. 224. (Translator's note: Also see supra, Part I, note 29.)

[32] Russia's share in the world tanker fleet was only 0.6 per cent on January 1, 1950. The world tanker fleet was then 2,062 units, with a total of 25,666,503 dead-weight tons. The Russians had only 21 units with 149,892 dead-weight tons. *Erdöl-Informationsdienst*, May 1, 1950.

[33] See Leimbach, *op.cit.*, pp. 421-422.

length is said to have tripled since then because of increasing demand and difficulty of access to the Arctic and Far East by railroad or highway.

All of these types of transportation are heavy consumers of fuel oil, lubricants, gasoline, and diesel motor oil. In 1937 the railroads used 2.5 million tons of fuel and lubricating oil. Navigation used 1.3 million tons.[34] The volume of increase in motor traffic during the last 12 years is shown by a comparison between 1937 and 1950. While in 1937 only 2,800,000 tons of gasoline were consumed (1,480,000 by motor traffic, 950,000 by agriculture, and 420,000 by the Soviet Army and other consumers), civilian consumption alone in 1950 was 7,500,-000 tons, three times that of 1937. The intensification of transportation and motorization in general is clearly demonstrated by this increase in gasoline consumption.

Agriculture: Important changes took place in agriculture with collectivization. The legal, economic, and organizational conditions of all of Russian agriculture have been radically altered. The European part of czarist Russia had 10.5 million small landholders and farmers with about 200 million acres of land, and about 30 thousand landowners with approximately 190 million acres of land. They used petroleum for illuminating purposes but not in tilling the soil. Today all the land is included in collectives (*kolkhoz*) or state farms (*sovkhoz*), which use farm machinery extensively. About 390 million acres of farm land today are worked for the largest part with mechanical energy. The tractor has become the symbol of Russian agriculture. In 1940 Russian agriculture operated 523,000 tractors, 182,-000 combines, and 228,000 trucks.[35] The fourth Five-Year Plan scheduled delivery of 325,000 tractors, 175,000 combines, 83,000 planters, and 112,000 motor plows. All this agricultural machinery—tractors, combines, threshing machines, planters, motor plows, and harvesters—is organized in 7,500 machinery tractor stations (MTS) to guarantee economical use. Marshal Bulganin said in his address on the occasion of the thirty-third anniversary of the October Revolution that the output in 1950 from new or repaired factories would be 4 times that in 1940 for "15-horsepower tractors, 3.8 times for com-

[34] See *ibid.*, pp. 421-422. See also Shimkin, *op.cit.*, p. 224.

[35] See Leimbach, *op.cit.*, p. 241; also Grigorjev, "Erfolge der Mechanisierung der Landwirtschaft in der Sowjetunion," *Neue Welt*, January 1950, p. 38. (Translator's note: At the beginning of 1951, Soviet agriculture employed 585,000 tractors, according to *Petroleum Press Service*, March 1952, p. 98. Also see "Farm Tractors in U.S.S.R. and Eastern Europe," *ibid.*, April 1952, pp. 142-143.)

bines, 4 times for motor plows, almost 6 times for motor planters, and 3 times for cultivators."

The average oil requirement of a tractor, planter, or combine can be easily computed. But making a correct estimate of oil consumption in Russian agriculture is difficult, because the number of working days cannot be determined with sufficient precision. However, the large number of tractors and machines used shows that the consumption of oil by agriculture must have increased considerably. In 1937 agriculture consumed no less than 5,650,000 tons of gasoline, naphtha, and kerosene.[36] According to the Soviets, agriculture was allocated one-third more oil products in 1950 than in 1949.

Home consumption: Kerosene is the chief oil product consumed in the home. In the years preceding World War I consumption of kerosene amounted to about 900,000 tons. Despite electrification of the country, the demand for kerosene is extremely high yet. In 1937 homes consumed 1.2 million tons of kerosene for illuminating purposes. It was estimated that consumption in 1950 would be approximately the same.[37]

The Soviet armed forces: Like industry, transportation, agriculture, and homes, the Soviet armed forces are large consumers of oil. Their actual demand can be estimated only roughly and their potential demand in war must be estimated by analogy. The Russian army had 175 divisions in 1950, of which 50 divisions (armored and artillery) were motorized.[38] The Russian submarine fleet, with 360 vessels, is a major consumer of oil. The Russian air force consisted in 1950 of a tactical force of 15,000 planes and a strategic force of about 1,000 planes (long-range bombers). The oil demand of such an air force is extremely high in peacetime for testing of machines and training of personnel. In war it increases manyfold. The consumption of the Russian air force in World War II gives an idea of the demand of an air force in war. In 1941 the Soviet Union received, through lend-lease from the United States, approximately 365,000 tons of high-octane aviation gasoline; in 1942, 180,000 tons; in 1943, 435,000 tons; and in 1944, about 730,000 tons. Despite these high deliveries,

---

[36] See Shimkin, *op.cit.*, p. 224. (Translator's note: He says that 8,080,000 barrels of gasoline, 7,200,000 barrels of heavy oil, and 29,450,000 barrels of kerosene were used by agriculture.)

[37] See *ibid.*, p. 224.

[38] Translator's note: The Soviet divisions have an average strength of about 8,200 men, according to the *New York Times*, July 13, 1952.

only a quarter of the Russian demand for aviation gasoline was covered.[39]

TABLE 20. Oil Consumption in the Soviet Union in 1937[40]
(thousands of tons)

Fuel Oil and Lubricants:	13,300
Shipping	1,300
Railroads	2,500
Power stations	900
Industry	6,600
Military and miscellaneous	2,000
Gasoline:	2,850
Agriculture	950
Trucking	1,480
Military and miscellaneous	420
Naphtha:	1,290
Agriculture	900
Military and miscellaneous	390
Kerosene:	5,580
Agriculture	3,800
Domestic	1,200
Military and miscellaneous	580
Total	23,020

These five chief consumers used in 1937, a year of peace, about 23 million tons of fuel oils, lubricants, gasoline, heavy gas oil, and kerosene, as Table 20 shows. It must be remembered that industrialization, motorization, and mechanization had by no means reached their present development in 1937, and, above all, that rearmament had not been undertaken to such an unusual extent.

A total consumption of 30 to 32 million tons can be assumed for 1950, which would call for a quantity of about 40 million tons of crude oil. One arrives at that figure if imports are added to the domestic oil production of 37.6 million tons and exports to China and North Korea are subtracted.

Various questions of production, consumption, and demand in the

[39] See Shimkin, *op.cit.*, p. 224.
[40] See *ibid.*, p. 224. (Translator's note: Export figures may be added, as follows: fuel oil and lubricants, 1,200,000 tons; gasoline, 200,000 tons; kerosene, 550,000 tons. This brings the total to 24,970,000 tons.)

Soviet Union, and the problem of balancing these factors will be discussed in detail in Part IV.

The Pattern of the Soviet Oil Industry

The peculiarity and importance of the Soviet oil industry can be best explained by comparison with the czarist oil industry. The main differences between the czarist and Soviet oil industries are shown in following comparisons:

1. In czarist time oil production was essentially limited to the oil fields in the Caucasus; that is, Baku, Groznyy, and Maykop. In Bolshevik times oil production has been considerably enlarged geographically, through the development of new oil-rich areas, especially in the region between the Urals and the Volga.

2. In imperial Russia the government prevented a sound development of its oil industry by shortsighted legislation; in Soviet Russia the government ensures rational production through legislation, except when overproduction is required during war, and promotes development of oil production through systematic scientific exploration.

3. In imperial Russia, oil production was based on the principle of free enterprise, which ruled the economic system of private capitalism. In Soviet Russia the oil industry is nationalized. It is ruled now by the principles of a socialistic economic system. The Soviet Union is thus the only important oil country where the oil industry is completely removed from the private initiative of free enterprise.

4. During the czarist regime foreign influence on the oil industry was extremely strong because of the large investments of foreign capital; in Soviet times foreign financial groups cannot invest or participate in the Russian oil industry. The Soviet Union is therefore the only major oil country where the oil industry is not involved in the network of the world-spanning international oil industry.

5. In czarist times there was only a comparatively small demand for oil products. In the first place, only fuel oil and kerosene were required. In Bolshevik times the demand for oil has increased tremendously, due to the transformation from an agrarian economy to an industrial economy. The question of a sufficient supply of oil products has become a serious political problem because of the high demand of the Soviet Union in peacetime and, what is more important, because of possible belligerent entanglements.

PART III

THE REGIONS OF THE SOVIET
OIL INDUSTRY

THE REGIONS OF THE SOVIET
OIL INDUSTRY

THE expression "oil industry" means here not only the oil industry in a narrow sense, but also the natural-gas and shale oil industries. In the foreground of the oil industry is, of course, oil production, but in some areas production of natural gas and shale oil is not insignificant.

The most important oil deposits of the Soviet Union lie west of the Ural Mountains. They stretch in two wide bands from the Caspian Sea to the west and north. East of the Urals there are only two considerable deposits of oil: in the Fergana Valley in Central Asia, and on Sakhalin Island in the Far East. However, since almost half the territory of the Soviet Union is covered by sedimentary formations where oil deposits could have been formed, the assumption is justified that in the future more oil deposits of commercial importance will be discovered in the Asiatic portion of the Union. Estimates of Russian oil reserves vary between 600 million tons (E. DeGolyer) and 20 billion tons (Egloff). The well-known Russian petroleum scientist, Gubkin, figured the oil supply of the Soviet Union in 1938 at 8.5 billion tons. These considerable differences can be explained by the fact that some of the estimates are based only on "proved" reserves and others on "probable" or "possible" reserves. This makes it the more important to consider the classification introduced by the Soviet Union in its decree of February 14, 1941. It distinguishes five categories of reserves; namely, A-1 ("absolutely proved"), A-2 ("thoroughly tested"), B ("sufficiently confirmed"), C-1 ("probable"), and C-2 ("possible"). To judge the value and importance of the oil industry, only those deposits can be considered that are confirmed by thorough exploration or at least ascertained with sufficient exactness. The terms "probable reserves" and "possible reserves" contain too many uncertain factors to be used for economic considerations. In applying this yardstick, Russian oil reserves are found to amount to one billion tons, which means that the Soviet Union has one tenth of the total proved reserves of world oil.[1]

[1] Translator's note: See *Petroleum Press Service*, March 1952, pp. 97-98: "According to the Soviet Technical press, known reserves of crude oil in the USSR have risen from less than 1,000 million tons (7 billion barrels more or less) in 1938 to 4,500 million tons (30 billion barrels more or less), the latest figure, being equivalent to about one hundred years' production at the present rate." *World Oil*, International Operations

Most natural gas is found with oil. All oil wells do not produce sufficient natural gas to warrant its industrial utilization, in which case the gas is used locally. The most important of the gas deposits of the Soviet Union which have more than local significance are those at Saratov on the Volga River, and at Dashava in the Western Ukraine. Some Soviet geologists estimate Russian gas reserves at 2.5 to 3.15 trillion cubic feet. Even if this estimate requires certain reservations, it should not be ignored since the Union has extremely rich gas deposits. In 1938 about 71 billion cubic feet, and in 1939 about 105 billion cubic feet were produced in Russia. This production corresponds in economic value to about 1,670,000 tons and 2,420,000 tons of petroleum, respectively.[2] Sixty billion cubic feet of gas were produced in 1946, 74.2 billion in 1947, 81.2 billion in 1948, and 83 billion in 1949. The fourth Five-Year Plan scheduled a gas production of 296.6 billion cubic feet for 1950, but actual production in that year may not have exceeded 122.5 billion cubic feet.[3] Shimkin attributes this deficit in the production of natural gas to the low quality of the gas, which makes higher production of gasoline impossible, to the lack of pumping equipment and pipelines, and finally to the fact that a large part of the gas must be returned to repressure oil reservoirs.

The total oil-shale reserves of the Soviet Union are estimated at about 55 billion tons. These rich oil-shale deposits make the Union, with the United States, Canada, Australia, and Manchuria, one of the most important oil-shale regions of the world. The largest Russian oil-shale deposits lie in Estonia and at the city of Gdov on Lake Peipus. There are also oil-shale deposits in the Ukhta-Pechora, Kirov, Kuybyshev, Saratov, Chelyabinsk, Syzran, and Vologda areas. These oil-shale deposits, however, are at present unexploited industrially, since economical extraction of shale oil from oil shale is a very difficult problem everywhere.

It seems convenient to group the descriptions of oil, gas, and oil-

---

Issue, July 15, 1952, p. 71, reports that world oil reserves on January 1, 1952 were 100,-477,560,000 barrels; and the *Oil and Gas Journal*, International Number, December 22, 1952, puts them at 118,151,200,000 barrels. On the crucial question of Soviet oil reserves, see *Erdöl und Kohle*, v (1952), 817-18.

[2] Generally 42,000 cubic feet of gas equal one ton of oil in value.

[3] See D. B. Shimkin, "Is Petroleum a Soviet Weakness?" the *Oil and Gas Journal*, December 21, 1950, p. 220. (Translator's note: See also *Petroleum Press Service, op.cit.*, p. 97. Production of natural gas is now increasing; the USSR's consumption in 1950 was 91,780,000,000 cubic feet.   ,

shale deposits around two recognized centers of the Russian oil industry, the Baku and Second Baku areas. As early as the czarist era Baku was the center of the Russian oil industry. It has been made the starting point for the survey of the southern and western regions. The Second Baku, developed by the Soviet government in the 1930's, has been made the starting point for the survey of the eastern regions. This geographic division coincides with Russian practice, which numbers Baku, Groznyy, Maykop, Georgia, Dagestan, Turkmenistan, and the Ukraine among the southwestern regions, and the Second Baku (with the fields of Molotov, Ufa, and Kuybyshev), Ukhta-Pechora, the Emba, Central Asia, and finally Sakhalin among the eastern regions.[4]

THE SOUTHWESTERN REGIONS

Baku

The oil area of Baku lies on the Apsheron Peninsula in Azerbaijan, one of the three Transcaucasian Soviet Socialist Republics. Its oil fields lie in a semicircle around Baku, the capital of Azerbaijan. Some of the fields which lie north and south of Baku on the Caspian coast are included in the Baku area despite their distance from that city (up to 100 miles).

The Baku oil region is the oldest in the Soviet Union. The fields of Sabunchi, Balakhany, and Romany[5] have produced oil without interruption since the 1870's. Bibi-Eybat joined these first producers in 1882 and shortly after 1900 was followed by Binagady and Surakhany. During the following decades 25 additional oil and gas fields were discovered.

Political division: The Baku oil fields are administered by the Azneft petroleum division, composed of the following trusts: Artemneft, Azizbekovneft, Beriyaneft, Buzovnyneft, Kaganovichneft, Kirovneft, Leninneft, Molotovneft, Ordzhonikidzeneft, and Stalinneft.

Oil fields: West of Baku lie the oil fields of Shubany, Saryncha, Gyulbakht, Shongar, Kergez, Kyzyl-Tepe, Puta, Lok-Batan, and Karadag, and the gas field of Miadzhik. North of Baku are located the oil fields of Sabunchi, Balakhany, Romany, Binagady, Buzovny, Maho-

---

[4] Data on Soviet fields, refineries, and pipelines are the result of a critical evaluation of German, English, and American publications, and especially of Russian trade journals and newspapers.

[5] Translator's note: Now named the Lenin fields.

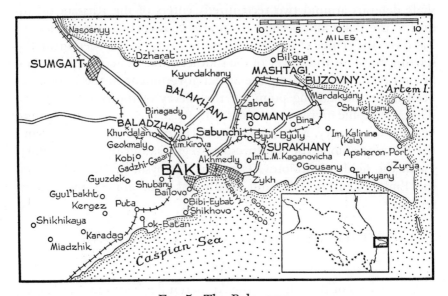

FIG. 5. The Baku area.

Reproduced from Shabad, *Geography of the USSR*
(New York: Columbia University Press, 1951).

medly, Fatmay, Baladzhary, Sian Shor, and Sulu Tepe. To the east
lie Surakhany, Kara Chukhur, Zykh, Kala, Peschany Island, and Artem Island. South of Baku lies the Bibi-Eybat oil field. On the coast
of the Caspian Sea, north of Baku, are located Shuraabad and Siazan
and, south of Baku, Pirsagat and Neftechala.

Almost all the oil deposits of the Baku area are located on anticlines.

Oil processing: Baku is not only the center of Russian oil production, but also the center of Russian oil refining. Five large refineries,
with an annual throughput capacity of about 18 million tons, including 2.5 million tons cracking capacity, operate in Baku.

Pipelines: Two pipelines originate in Baku. The older pipeline
from Baku to Batumi was built between 1896 and 1906 for 20 million
rubles. It is a 550-mile, 8-inch line with an annual capacity of about
one million tons. It is designed for the transportation of petroleum
only. The second pipeline from Baku to Batumi was completed in
1928, and has a length of 510 miles, a diameter of 10 inches, and an
annual capacity of about 1.4 million tons.

Oil production: Before the October Revolution Baku was the undisputed center of Russian oil production. The Baku area produced about 8 million tons of oil in 1916, compared with about 1.5 million tons produced in the Groznyy district, 265,000 tons in the Emba district, 32,000 tons in the Maykop district, and 16,000 tons on Cheleken Island.

During the expansion of the oil industry under the Soviets, Baku increased its production steadily from about 7.8 million tons in 1916 to about 22 million tons in 1940. From then on, however, signs of depletion appeared in the fields and would have been more pronounced but for successful offshore drilling and new discoveries, which compensated, in part at least, for this decline in the old fields. These circumstances were taken into consideration, and the production goal for the Baku area was only about 17 million tons in 1950. This goal was reached according to plan. Baku's share of the total production prior to World War I was about 90 per cent and in 1940 about 70 per cent; today it has been reduced to only 45 per cent. Despite the absolute and comparative decline in its production, Baku's aggregate production is remarkable enough. Its oil fields have produced about 700 million tons of oil in 80 years. This extraordinary performance is due to Baku's favorable geological conditions. Oil deposits are not lost in a wide area but are concentrated in the narrowest space. Up to 22 successive producing horizons are found in that area, giving Baku an outstanding position among the oil regions of the globe.[6] In addition to these oil deposits, Baku also has natural-gas deposits, especially at Bibi-Eybat, Surakhany, and Miadzhik. Some of these gas deposits were exploited for industrial and household use before World War II.

Transportation: Facilities for the transportation of Baku's oil are as follows:

1. Tankers going to another Caspian Sea port—to Astrakhan, which sends oil up the Volga to Central Russia; Krasnovodsk, which sends it to Turkmenistan; or Makhachkala, from where the oil can be carried by pipeline via Groznyy to Rostov, and then shipped to the Ukraine.

2. Pipelines from Baku to Batumi, from where the oil can be shipped by tanker to the large oil transit ports of the Black Sea and the Sea of Azov—Odessa, Nikolayev, Kherson, Sevastopol, Zhdanov, and Novorossiysk—and from there to Western Russia.

[6] Translator's note: See *World Oil Atlas* (Houston, 1948) for an excellent survey of Baku and other Russian oil areas.

3. The Caucasian railroad network.

In 1937 the amounts of oil transported from Baku were: about 5 million tons via Astrakhan and the Volga, about 2.1 million tons via Krasnovodsk, about 6.3 million tons via Makhachkala and Groznyy, and 3.2 million tons via Batumi and the Black Sea. It can be assumed that present figures show similar proportions.

Despite these favorable shipping facilities, the disadvantages of Baku's location cannot be overlooked. In the first place the shipping routes from Baku to the interior markets, such as the Donets region, the Ukraine, Moscow, and Leningrad, are very long. Also Baku's location on the extreme frontier of the Soviet Union would be dangerously exposed in the event of a military conflict, for it can be reached by airplane from Iran and the Eastern Mediterranean in a very short time.

Groznyy

The Groznyy oil district, lying on the northeastern slope of the Caucasus Mountains in the territory of the Russian Soviet Federated Socialist Republic, was at one time second only to Baku, the Union's largest producer. Oil has been produced in the Old Groznyy field since 1890 and in the New Groznyy field since 1913. In 1910 production from the Groznyy region passed the one-million-ton mark. Although lagging far behind Baku, Groznyy's output always held second rank among the Russian fields until recently, when it yielded that position to the Second Baku district.

Political division: Groznyy oil fields belong to the Grozneft oil group, with its Malgobekneft, Oktyabrneft, Staragrozneft, and Tashkalaneft trusts.

Oil fields: In the immediate neighborhood of Groznyy lie the Old Groznyy, New Groznyy, and Gunuski fields. West of Groznyy lie Malgobek, Voznessenka, Bakovichi, Alkasovo, Ali Yurt, and Gorski. Of the other fields, Gudermes lies east of Groznyy, Makhkety southeast of Groznyy, and the natural-gas field of Pravoberezhnoye north of Groznyy.

All oil deposits in the Groznyy area are located on anticlines which have a highly complex structure because of tectonic faults. It is interesting to note that the Groznyy fields also have up to 22 sand sections, of which, however, no more than 13 are petroliferous.

Oil processing: Groznyy is, next to Baku, the most important center in the Russian refining industry. Three large refineries are in

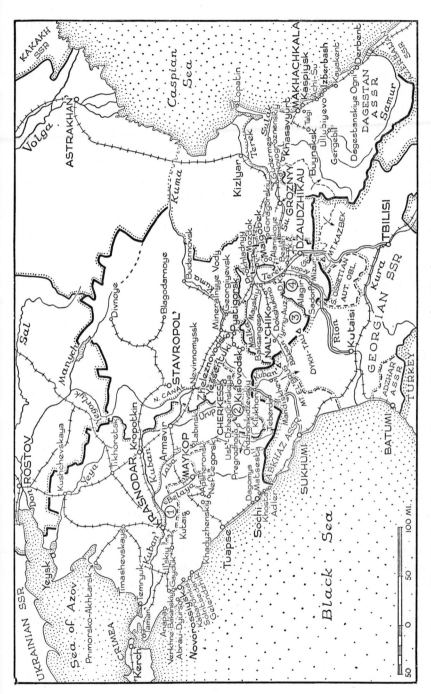

Fig. 6. The Northern Caucasus: Georgia, Dagestan, the Maykop area, and the Grozny area. Reproduced from Shabad, *Geography of the USSR* (New York: Columbia University Press, 1951).

operation at present, with an annual throughput capacity of about 7.5 million tons, including a cracking capacity of about 2.5 million tons. This high capacity was planned on the assumption that the Groznyy area would become as important as the Baku area. When production lagged far behind the potential refining capacity it was decided to process Baku oil in the Groznyy refineries.

Pipelines: Groznyy is a crossroad of the Soviet pipeline system. Two large pipelines have their origin there. One extends via Armavir and Maykop to Tuapse on the Black Sea; the other via Armavir and Rostov to Trudovaya, and from there construction via Stalino to Dnepropetrovsk on the Dnieper is planned. In addition, Groznyy is the terminus of two pipelines from Makhachkala, the pipeline from Malgobek, and the natural-gas pipeline from Pravoberezhnoye.

Oil production: Oil production in the Groznyy fields increased steadily from 1920 to 1932, when it reached its peak of 7.7 million tons. It then dropped rapidly, reaching about 2.4 million tons in 1940. Production in 1950 was 1.8 million tons. From the discovery of the first Groznyy oil field until 1950, a total of 100 million tons of oil was produced in this area. Chief producers were the Old Groznyy, New Groznyy, and Malgobek fields.

The Old Groznyy field, the first in this area, has produced a considerable amount of natural gas. Between 1893 and 1950, Old Groznyy produced about 35 million tons, reaching the one-million-ton mark in 1910. Production declined gradually from 1925 until 1934, when new discoveries temporarily halted this decline to some extent. Despite its almost 60 years of exploitation, Old Groznyy still keeps some significance among the Groznyy oil fields.

New Groznyy followed Old Groznyy as the most productive field in the Groznyy area and the increased production of the district was due essentially to New Groznyy's high rate of production. Since 1932, however, the entire Groznyy district has shown a drop in production along with New Groznyy. Total production from 1913 to 1950 was 52 million tons, and today New Groznyy is of small importance.

Except for Old and New Groznyy, Malgobek is the largest field in the area, and with its discovery the decrease in total production was delayed for a time. Drilling in this field began in 1927 but only gas was found. The first oil well was drilled in 1933. Intensive operations followed and production reached 961,000 tons in 1938, which placed Malgobek at the top of the Groznyy fields, as shown in Table 21.

TABLE 21.   Oil Production in the Groznyy Fields in 1938
(tons)

Malgobek	961,000
New Groznyy	927,000
Old Groznyy	300,000
Other fields	512,000
Total	2,700,000

Compared with these three (Malgobek, Old Groznyy, and New Groznyy), the other fields are insignificant.

The rise, peak, and decline of Groznyy oil production can be seen in the following table:

TABLE 22.   Oil Production in the Groznyy Area from 1921 to 1940
(millions of tons)

1921	1.3	1931	7.3
1922	1.5	1932	7.7
1923	1.4	1933	4.9
1924	1.8	1934	3.4
1925	2.1	1935	3.3
1926	2.6	1936	3.1
1927	3.1	1937	2.9
1928	3.8	1938	2.7
1929	4.6	1939	2.4
1930	6.9	1940	2.4

Maykop

The Maykop area lies on the northern edge of the Western Caucasus and extends about 187 miles from Maykop in the east to Kerch on the Crimean Peninsula in the west. This oil district also belongs to the Russian Soviet Federated Socialist Republic. Its deposits were discovered in 1908. The oldest and most important fields lie in a triangle formed by the cities of Krasnodar, Maykop, and Tuapse. This is the center of Maykop oil production. Additional fields lie to the west of this triangle, extending across the Taman Peninsula into the Crimea. Before World War I Maykop's oil production ranked third, after Baku and Groznyy. It lost this place to the Second Baku, which has also displaced Groznyy.

Political division: The Maykop oil fields belong to the Krasnodarneft group, with its three trusts: Apsheronneft, Chadysneft, and Chernomorneft.

[73]

Oil fields: In the triangle formed by Krasnodar, Maykop, and Tuapse lie the fields of Apsheronsk (Maykop), Wax Mountain, Khadyzhenskiy, Asphalt Mountain, Shiraki, Kura Tsitse, Abuzy, Kutais, Sepsil, and Kaluyski. West of Krasnodar lie the fields of Ilskiy, Krymsky-Kudako, Keslerovo-Varenikovo, and Adaghum. The field of Suvorov-Cherkess is located on the Taman Peninsula and the field of Changelek in the Eastern Crimea.

Most of these deposits are associated with monoclines.

Oil processing: The oil produced in Maykop is refined at Krasnodar and Tuapse. The Krasnodar refinery has a throughput capacity of 1,250,000 tons. The Tuapse refinery is the terminus of the pipeline from Groznyy and processes crude oil from other areas also. Its throughput capacity is 1,750,000 tons, including a cracking capacity of 500,000 tons.

Pipelines: The Maykop oil fields are connected with the Krasnodar refinery by pipeline, permitting direct shipment from the fields to the refinery. In addition, the large Groznyy-Armavir-Tuapse pipeline traverses the area.

Oil production: Prior to World War I, oil production in the Maykop fields increased rapidly. It exceeded 100,000 tons in 1911 and 1912 (the peak year) but then declined precipitously. It rose again after the October Revolution with the intensification of development. By the end of the 1920's, production had reached half a million tons. Between 1930 and 1940 it was increased 500,000 tons, to more than 2 million tons.

TABLE 23. Development of Oil Production in the Maykop Area
(thousands of tons)

1930	500	1936	1,200
1931	530	1937	1,650
1932	910	1938	2,000
1933	920	1939	2,200
1934	940	1940	2,200
1935	1,180		

Present total production in the Maykop area is 1.5 million tons.

Georgia

Shiraki and Mirzaani, the two Georgian fields, lie in the Georgian Soviet Socialist Republic, east of Tbilisi, the capital. Both fields are situated on anticlinal folds. Production started in the early 1930's and was estimated at 330,000 tons for 1939. Present production may be around 120,000 tons. Indications of oil are numerous in Georgia; for instance, in Norio Martkabi,[7] north of Tbilisi, and on the Black Sea coast at Sabsa Ompareti. So far no discoveries with possibilities of commercial production have been reported. A 25-mile pipeline connects the Shiraki and Mirzaani oil fields with the city of Kachreti.

Georgia has three refineries, located in Mirzaani, Tbilisi, and Batumi, the terminus of the Baku-Batumi pipeline.

The operation of the fields and refineries is controlled by the independent Gruzneft trust.

Dagestan

The oil area of Dagestan lies on the coast of the Caspian Sea, adjacent to and north of the Baku area. It extends from the city of Derbent to the city of Makhachkala, thus falling in the territory of the Russian Soviet Federated Socialist Republic.

The most important fields are Berekei, Kayakent, Izberbash, and Achi-Su. There are also two gas fields, Dag Ogni and Duzlak. These deposits are located in part on anticlinal folds, and in part on dome-like folds or uplifts (as at Berekei, Dag Ogni, and Duzlak). The area was not explored before the second Five-Year Plan. The first successful well was drilled in 1934. Commercial production commenced in 1936 and was estimated at 250,000 tons in 1939. Present production may exceed 500,000 tons.

A refinery is located in Makhachkala and processes both Dagestan and Baku oil.

A 37-mile pipeline connecting Izberbash with Makhachkala was opened in 1939. Also originating in Makhachkala are two important pipelines constructed in 1924 and 1935, each with a length of 97 miles and each connecting the coast of the Caspian Sea with Groznyy.

Dagestan belongs to the independent Dagneft trust.

The Turkmen Area

The oil deposits of the Caucasian region extend from Baku northwest through Georgia, Dagestan, Groznyy, and Maykop to the Crimea, and extend beyond the Caspian Sea in an easterly direction. Oil production began before World War I on the Island of Cheleken, just

[7] Translator's note: The author errs. Norio and Novo Martkabi are two different prospects.

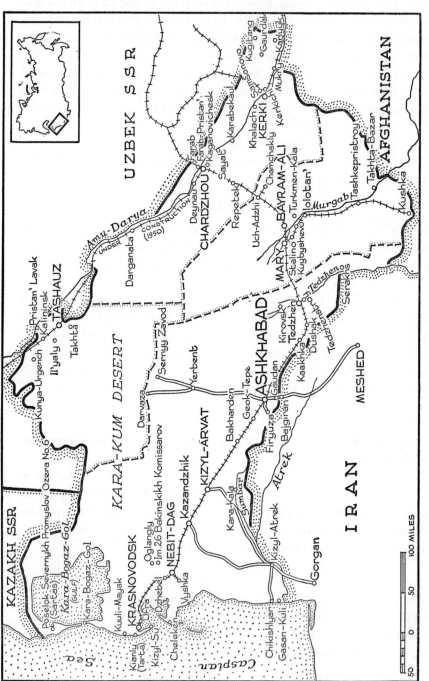

Fig. 7. The Turkmen Soviet Socialist Republic.

Reproduced from Shabad, *Geography of the USSR* (New York: Columbia University Press, 1951).

off the Turkmenian coast in the Caspian Sea. Oil fields were developed on the continent after the October Revolution. Production there compensated for the steady decline in production on Cheleken which began in 1913, and lent new significance to the Turkmenian oil industry.

In 1938, production in the Turkmenian fields amounted to about 300,000 tons. The third Five-Year Plan scheduled an increase in production to 1,150,000 tons in 1942. However, it was impossible to reach this goal. The fourth Five-Year Plan scheduled a production of about 1.1 million tons for 1950. Actual production in 1950 may have been between 1.2 million tons and 1.3 million tons.

Political division: The independent Turkmenneft trust administers the Turkmenian oil fields.

Oil fields: In addition to the oil field on Cheleken Island, which is still productive, there are the fields of Nebit-Dag, Neftedag, and, about 140 miles to the east, the field of Mangshlak. In the southwestern corner of Turkmenistan, near the Iranian border, is the field of Chikishlyar.

The Nebit-Dag and Neftedag fields are on anticlines; the Cheleken field is located on a faulted dome.

Oil processing: Two refineries serve this area: the refinery at Nebit-Dag processes oil produced in that field, and the refinery at Krasnovodsk refines oil from Baku. The latter has a throughput capacity of 200,000 tons and a cracking capacity of 150,000 tons.

Pipelines: A 300-mile line supplying Eastern Turkmenistan originates at Krasnovodsk and terminates at Ashkhabad, the capital of Turkmenistan. It carries no crude oil, only finished products.

The Central Ukraine

The Ukrainian Soviet Socialist Republic has—apart from the oil in the Western Ukraine (Carpathian Mountains), which will be treated separately—only two rather unimportant oil fields at Romny and Poltava, both lying on salt domes. During the general prospecting, considerable exploration, following oil indications, was carried out between Kiev and Kharkov. The geological exploration confirmed that there exist oil-bearing structures in the trough-fault between the Donets and Dnieper Rivers; commercial production, however, has been small; it is at present about 30,000 tons and of only local importance. The Central Ukrainian oil fields are under administration of the independent Ukrneft trust.

Fig. 8. The Ukrainian Soviet Socialist Republic.

roduced from Shabad, *Geography of the USSR* (New York: Columbia University Press, 1951).

The Western Ukraine

The oil fields lying on the eastern slope of the Carpathians between Przemysl and Chernovtsy (Cernauti) are the world's oldest, and have truly had a checkered history. They changed political rulers several times during the First and Second World Wars.

Oil production was begun in these fields in 1860, but systematic operation did not begin until 1874. The production curve for the area resembles a huge arch with a peak production in 1909 of 2 million tons. From there the curve descends just as evenly as it rose. The fields were badly damaged in World War I and, as a result, production fell as low as 800,000 tons (in 1918). These Galician fields passed at the end of World War I from Austria-Hungary to the new Poland, under which regime the drop in production continued. (See Table 24.)

TABLE 24. Oil Production in the Carpathian Fields from 1930 to 1939

Year	Production in the Carpathian Fields (thousands of tons)	Total Polish Production (thousands of tons)
1930	440	660
1931	390	630
1932	330	555
1933	325	550
1934	300	530
1935	285	515
1936	270	510
1937	270	500
1938	270	507
1939	250	530

After Poland's defeat in World War II, the Carpathian oil fields became part of the Soviet Union. That was in 1939. Two years later, when Germany attacked Russia, they were occupied by the German army, which remained four years. Production of oil and gas in those years, 1941 to 1944, is shown in Table 25, below. After World War II the Russians regained the Carpathian fields and incorporated them into the territory of the Ukrainian Soviet Socialist Republic.[8]

Production under the Polish administration (1918-1939) and under the German occupation affords a clue to the capacity of the area. The fourth Five-Year Plan scheduled for the Western Ukraine a

8 Translator's note: See p. 82, n. 9.

TABLE 25. Oil and Gas Production in the Carpathian Fields
from 1941 to 1944

Year	Oil Production (thousands of tons)	Gas Production (billions of cubic feet)
1941	130	7.4
1942	260	18.7
1943	255	22.2
1944	140	15.7

production in line with its past performance. Combined with the small fields of the Central Ukraine, it was expected to yield 325,000 tons in 1950.

Political division: The Western Ukraine (Carpathian) fields belong to the independent Ukrneft trust.

Oil fields: The oil and gas fields of the Western Ukraine lie roughly in the triangle formed by Przemysl, Lvov, and Chernovtsy.

The city of Borislav is the commercial oil center in the area, the city of Dashava the gas center, and the city of Drogobych the refining center. The oil and gas fields in general are small and lie northwest and southwest of Borislav, Dashava, and Drogobych. The oil fields are Borislav, Lodyna, Rosochy, Strzelbice, Ploskie, Graziowa, Czarna, Polana, Opaka, Nahujowice, Skhodnitsa-Urycez, Pereginsko, Majdan, Sloboda-Rungurska, Kosmach, Orow, Lipiz, Wolica-Kroscienko, Bistrie, Holoweko, Lomna, Wolosianka-Mala, Jasienica, Solna, Mraznica, Dolina, Kropiwnik, Witwica, Sloboda-Nybielowska, Starunia, Markowa, and Porohy. The gas fields are Dashava, Borislav, Rypne, Bytkov, and Pasieczna.

Practically all these fields are located on anticlines.

Oil processing: All oil produced in this area, except for small amounts, is refined in Drogobych and Lvov. Small refineries are located at Stryy, Nadvornaya, and Strzelbice.

Pipelines: Two natural-gas pipelines originate in the important Dashava gas field. One terminates in Lvov. The other, 350 miles long and completed in 1947, terminates in Kiev, with a branch to Vinnitsa, and supplies gas to industry and homes in its area.

Oil and gas production: Production of oil in 1950 totalled 300,000 tons. After decades of exploitation, the small fields cannot produce larger quantities even with the application of modern drilling and production methods. Since it is the only oil production in that part of the Union, however, it is valuable in supplying local requirements.

Gas production is far more important. Dashava's fields are second in size in the Soviet Union only to the Saratov gas fields on the Volga River. Both Lvov (population, 320,000) and Kiev (population, 850,-000) are supplied with gas from the Dashava fields. In 1943 gas production from the Dashava fields totalled 2.2 billion cubic feet, corresponding to 530,000 tons of crude oil.[9]

Oil Shale in Estonia

The Estonian oil-shale deposits are by far the most significant, economically, in all Russia. They lie at Kokhtla-Yarve in the northeastern corner of the Soviet Socialist Republic of Estonia. Their existence was known before World War I, but commercial production only began after 1918, when Estonia became an independent nation. The first company to operate in Estonia was established in 1922. At first oil shale was used as fuel by industry and the railroads. Later Estonia began to extract oil from the shale. Like the Western Ukraine, the Estonian oil-shale region went through a period of radical change. From 1918 to 1940, Estonia was an independent nation. From 1940 to 1941 it belonged to Soviet Russia, from 1941 to 1944 it was occupied by Germany, and in 1944 the Russians retook it.

The oil-shale strata are only 33 feet deep and are an average of about 7 feet in thickness. They cover an area of about 1,500 square miles and on the east extend into old Russian territory. The deposits at Gdov on Lake Peipus can be considered a continuation of the Estonian oil-shale regions. The Estonian oil-shale deposits are estimated at five billion tons.[10] Since oil content runs as high as 20 per cent, theoretically one billion tons of crude oil could be extracted from the deposits. Production of Estonian oil shale and shale oil increased steadily before World War II.

In 1939 the shale-oil production from Estonian oil shale was 15,000 tons a month and 180,000 tons a year. In 1950 about 4 million tons of oil shale were produced, out of which 450,000 tons of crude oil

[9] Translator's note: As a result of an agreement in 1951 between Russia and Poland, the Soviet Union returned some of the Polish oil fields to Poland. They were in full operation and equipped with the latest Soviet drilling equipment. The fields returned account for 20 per cent of the total Polish production. They are under the control of a newly established government-owned company, Ustrzyckie Kopalnictwo Naftowe, with headquarters in Ustrzykie Dolne. The industry in Poland began the manufacture of drilling equipment in 1951. *Erdöl und Kohle*, v (1952), 393.

[10] See *Erdöl und Kohle*, III (1950), 148.

FIG. 9. The Baltic region, including Estonia.

Reproduced from Shabad, *Geography of the USSR*
(New York: Columbia University Press, 1951).

were extracted. The schedule for 1950 (8 million tons of oil shale and 1 million tons of crude oil) could not be reached. However, compared with this production in Estonia, the yield of oil shale in other Soviet areas was small.

TABLE 26. Development of the Estonian Oil-Shale Industry
between 1934 and 1939
(thousands of tons)

	1934	1935	1936	1937	1938	1939
Oil shale produced	589	604	767	1,136	1,474	1,667
Used as fuel	346	253	423	538	707	657
Distilled	243	351	344	598	767	1,010
Crude shale oil obtained by distillation	47	47	64	112	140	180

Unless the oil shale produced is used for fuel by industry or the railroads, it must be distilled by special installations, such as shaft kilns or retorts. Such distillation plants exist in the Kokhtla-Yarve area, in addition to processing and refining installations where gasoline, diesel oils, and lubricating oil can be manufactured from shale oil. The Russian Baltic fleet has first call on these finished products.

A 125-mile gas pipeline was constructed in 1947 and 1948 from Kokhtla-Yarve to Leningrad to transmit the gas resulting from Estonian shale-oil production. It supplies one third of Leningrad's population. A gas pipeline to Tallin (formerly Reval) is under construction.

THE EASTERN REGIONS

The oil deposits of Dagestan, Georgia, and the Central Ukraine, which were mentioned above as having been opened up during the Soviet regime, are comparatively of little significance in the Russian oil industry. However, the discovery of the Second Baku oil deposits by Soviet petroleum geologists between 1930 and 1940 represents an important milestone in the history of Russian oil, and its importance cannot be minimized in spite of the fact that some isolated spots have not fulfilled expectations.

The Second Baku is an area approximately the size of Spain.[11] It lies in the eastern part of European Russia, in a rough quadrangle formed

[11] Translator's note: i.e., about 190,000 square miles.

by the cities of Kirov and Molotov in the north and Saratov and Chkalov in the south. Adjacent to it on the north is the Ukhta-Pechora oil region and on the south, the Emba oil region. The Ural Mountains form the eastern border and the Volga River forms the western border at the present. These limits are not definite because in recent years numerous indications of oil have been observed, not only on the eastern slope of the Urals but also on the western bank of the Volga, and farther extension, particularly to the west, is probable. According to the most recent Russian publications, promising test wells have been drilled at Penza, Ivanovo, Ryizan, and Tula, south of Moscow. A deep test at Kaluga is said to have been completed as a producing well.

To correct a widespread erroneous opinion, the Second Baku is not an oil province in which oil field is linked to oil field in uninterrupted succession. On the contrary! Nevertheless, since petroliferous structures occur here in such abundance, it is not misleading to group these deposits under a single name.

The name Second Baku, which associates this area with that of the first Baku on the Caspian Sea, might lead to the conclusion that the two regions have certain geological structures and economic conditions in common. But this is not the case. Important economic and geological differences exist. Whereas the oil deposits of the original Baku are concentrated in a narrow area, the oil fields of the Second Baku are widely separated. Oil in Baku comes from as many as 22 commercially productive petroleum horizons, which explains its high production. In the Second Baku only two or three successive producing horizons have been proved to exist. Therefore, the root of the name Second Baku is not so much scientific or economic as it is propagandistic. The name was coined with the hope that an oil region had been discovered that would rank with the original Baku region.

Four centers stand out in this tremendous territory: the cities of Molotov (formerly Perm), Ufa, Kuybyshev, and Saratov. The oil and gas fields in the vicinities of these four cities constitute the basis for the oil wealth of the Second Baku. The fields around Molotov, Ufa, and Kuybyshev produce oil; those around Saratov, natural gas. Asphalt, a surface indication of oil, has long been seen and is mentioned in ancient literature. But such indications did not assume real significance until the latter half of the last century. Several unsuccessful test wells were drilled in various places around the turn of the century. The outbreak of the First World War plus the Revolution and its aftermath crippled further exploration for a number of years. At the end of the 1920's, systematic geological and geophysical exploration was resumed. To the Soviet geologist I. M. Gubkin is due credit for having directed general attention to this area. His theories were confirmed by actual drilling when the first oil deposit was discovered at Verkhne-Chusovskiye Gorodki, near Molotov, in 1929. There followed the discovery of the Ishimbay oil field in the Ufa region in 1935, the Syzran oil field in the Kuybyshev area in 1935, and the first Saratov gas field in 1942. The greatest development in the production of oil and the construction of refineries and pipelines occurred during the third Five-Year Plan. The development of the Second Baku was considered one of the most important and urgent aims of that Plan. Intensive geophysical prospecting and drilling of test wells in the years following resulted in the discovery of new oil structures, which increased the Second Baku production from year to year. (See Table 27.)

TABLE 27. Development of Oil Production in the Second Baku Region[12]
(thousands of tons)

1929	0.6	1938	1,300.0
1932	10.0	1939	1,850.0
1933	35.0	1940	3,000.0
1934	75.0	1946	6,000.0
1935	412.0	1947	7,500.0
1936	650.0	1950	10,600.0
1937	980.0		

The chief production centers are the Tuymazy fields in the Ufa region and the Syzran fields in the Kuybyshev area. In considering past and potential developments it should not be disregarded that drilling in the Second Baku meets with the greatest difficulty, due to the frequent occurrence of rock as hard as crystalline rock.[13]

With a production of 10.6 million tons, the Second Baku's share of

[12] Translator's note: *Petroleum Press Service* gives for 1950 a production figure for the Second Baku region of 16.4 million tons. "No regional split up is available for 1951 but it has been announced that the annual production plans were more than fulfilled in all parts of the Second Baku area. No similar claim has been made for production at Baku." However, offshore drilling in the Caspian Sea exceeded its production target. *Petroleum Press Service, op.cit.,* p. 97.

[13] Translator's note: Another disadvantage of oil from the Second Baku region is its high sulphur content. See A. M. Leeston, *Magic Oil, Servant of the World* (Dallas, 1951), p. 145; also J. G. Tolpin in his review of the original German edition of the present book in *Petroleum Times*, March 1952, p. 189.

the total Russian production is about 28 per cent. Among the oil regions of Russia, the Second Baku occupies second place, after Baku. The great importance of the Second Baku became evident for the first time in the Second World War, when the oil fields in the Ukraine, Maykop, and part of the Groznyy district were put out of operation, and their loss had to be compensated for by the newly discovered fields. Today the special significance of the Second Baku lies in its geographical location. It is in the heart of the Soviet Union, between the industrial district of Central Russia around Moscow and the industrial region of the Urals. Its favorable location near the large consumers is further enhanced by advantageous traffic facilities. This region has a well-developed network of railroads and two important waterways, the Volga and Kama Rivers, and also is connected directly with the capital, Moscow, by the Volga-Moskva Canal. Another important factor is that this area is in less danger militarily than the Caucasian fields, which lie near the international border.

Since the four principal oil and gas regions are separated from each other by hundreds of miles despite the occasional fields lying between them, it seems sensible to discuss each of these regions and their operation, including refineries and pipelines, separately.[14]

The Molotov[15] Oil Region

The oil area of Molotov lies west of the Central Urals, approximately halfway between the cities of Kirov and Sverdlovsk. Discovery of the first indications of oil deposits took place at Verkhne-Chusovskiye Gorodki in 1929 and was incidental to exploration for potassium. This discovery was the impetus for intensive and systematic exploration. In a few years the existence of several considerable oil deposits was proved. The first oil was discovered at Krasnokamsk in 1934 and the first deep well was drilled in 1936. Oil was discovered at Severokamsk in 1938.

Political division: The Molotov fields are governed by the Molotovneft group, which consists of the Krasnokamneft and Severokamneft trusts.

Oil fields: Near Gorodki, east of Molotov, lies the field of Verkhne-

14 See S. F. Fjodorov, "Laws of Geological Structure in the Oil and Gas Deposits of the Ural-Volga Area," in the *Journal of Soviet Science*, 1949, No. 4, pp. 167ff., and S. J. Mironov, "The Oil Wealth of the Ural-Volga Area and the Requirements for Its Further Exploration," *Journal of Soviet Science*, 1948, No. 2, pp. 132ff.

15 Translator's note: Formerly Perm, from which the geological term "Permian" is derived.

Fig. 10. The Central Urals, including the Molotov area.

Reproduced from Shabad, *Geography of the USSR*
(New York: Columbia University Press, 1951).

Chusovskiye Gorodki, while the Polazna field is north of Molotov. The fields of Severokamsk, Krasnokamsk, Overiata, and Shilovo are to the west. All these fields lie on anticlines except Verkhne-Chusovskiye Gorodki, which lies on a buried reef.

Oil processing: Two refineries are in this area. One, in Molotov, has an annual throughput capacity of 600,000 tons, including an annual cracking capacity of 200,000 tons. The other, in Gorodki, has an annual throughput capacity of 1,400,000 tons, including an annual cracking capacity of 250,000 tons.

Pipelines: The Molotov fields, located on the Kama River and frequently called the Kama fields, are crossed by a gas pipeline, 500 miles in length, which originates in the Izhma gas field in the Ukhta-Pechora region and terminates in the area of Izhevsk, southwest of Molotov.

The Ufa Oil Region

The Ufa oil region lies in the piedmont of the Southern Urals, west of Magnitogorsk. Its most important deposits are located at Ishimbay and Tuymazy, south and west, respectively, of Ufa.

In the southern part, indications of oil have been observed for a long time. Several tests were drilled between 1900 and 1920, without practical results. On the initiative of Gubkin, the geologist, systematic geological exploration was begun in 1929. The first deep well was drilled in 1931. The first wells were brought in as gushers at Ishimbay and Buranchino in 1933. The oil-bearing strata are up to 500 feet thick at some places.

The oil deposits at Tuymazy lie about 90 miles west of Ufa. Surface indications were completely lacking here. The first well was drilled in the spring of 1937 at Tuymazy, and was brought in as a gusher from a depth of 3,300 feet. The oil comes from a sandy limestone clay bed. In the Second Baku, the Tuymazy oil field is second only to the Syzran field at Kuybyshev in size and richness. A city of oil workers called Oktyabrskiy, with over 100,000 inhabitants, has arisen here in recent years.

Political division: The oil fields of the Ufa district are administered by the Bashneft oil group, which is subdivided into two trusts, Ishimbayneft and Tuymazyneft.

Oil fields: About 90 miles south of Ufa, on both sides of the Belaya River, lie the fields of Ishimbay, Kusiankul, Smakaevo, Buranchino,

Fig. 11. The Urals, including the Ufa and Molotov areas.

Reproduced from Shabad, *Geography of the USSR* (New York: Columbia University Press, 1951)

Termen-yelga, Allaguvatovo, and Kusminovka. To the west of Ufa, also at a distance of about 90 miles, lies the field of Tuymazy. All the fields of the Ufa region lie on buried reefs, with the exception of Smakaevo, which is on a diapir fold.

Oil processing: This area is outstanding as an oil-processing center. Ufa's refineries have a throughput capacity of 1,400,000 tons, Sterlitamak's have 750,000 tons, and Ishimbay's have 450,000 tons. The capacity at Tuymazy is not known.

Pipelines: The oil fields both to the south and west are connected by pipeline with Ufa. Two 100-mile pipelines[16] were constructed in 1939 and 1940 from Ishimbay to Ufa. A 90-mile pipeline,[17] which was completed in 1940, originates in Tuymazy and terminates in Ufa.

The Kuybyshev Oil Region

The oil deposits of Kuybushev lie in part in the big loop of the Volga River at Kuybyshev and in part to the east of Kuybyshev, some as far as about 100 miles away. The Syzran field in the Volga loop was discovered in 1935 and started producing in 1937. The Yablonovo field at Stavropol was discovered in 1937 and has been producing since 1938. The Buguruslan field was discovered in 1937 and has been producing oil and gas since 1938.

Political division: The fields west of Kuybyshev and the fields at Kinel are administered by the Kuybyshevneft group with its three trusts: Stavropolneft, Syzranneft, and Kinelneft. The fields east of Kuybyshev, Buguruslan and Sultangulovo, are administered by the independent Buguruslanneft trust.

Oil fields: The field of Yablonovo is located west of Kuybyshev, the Syzran field is in the Volga loop, the Kinel field is about 62 miles east of Kuybyshev, the Buguruslan oil and gas field is about 100 miles east of Kuybyshev, and farthest east lies the gas field of Sultangulovo. The Syzran and Yablonovo fields lie on domes and the Buguruslan field is on an anticline.

Oil processing: Three refineries are operating in this area, at Kuybyshev, Syzran, and Buguruslan, but their capacity is not known.

Pipelines: A pipeline from Yablonovo via Batraki to Syzran was built between 1940 and 1947. A gas pipeline was built in 1947 from the newly discovered Sultangulovo field to Buguruslan. The field of

16 Translator's note: With six-inch diameter.
17 Translator's note: With 12-inch diameter.

Buguruslan was connected with the city of Kuybyshev in 1943 by a gas pipeline.[18]

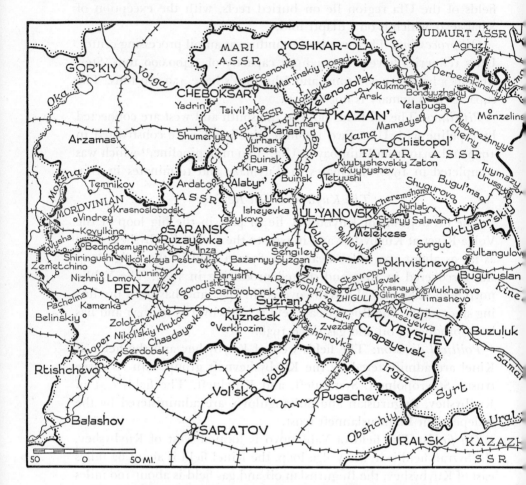

FIG. 12. The Middle Volga region, including the Kuybyshev area.

Reproduced from Shabad, *Geography of the USSR* (New York: Columbia University Press, 1951).

The Saratov Natural-Gas Area

The Saratov area, between Kuybyshev and Stalingrad, contains Russia's most important natural-gas deposits. It supplies not only Saratov but also Moscow with natural gas. This area is more important than the Dashava gas field in the Western Ukraine, which has been exploited for some time. At Saratov methane gas was discovered as

[18] Translator's note: This pipeline is 97 miles long and ten inches in diameter.

FIG. 13. The Lower Volga region, including the Saratov area.

Reproduced from Shabad, *Geography of the USSR*
(New York: Columbia University Press, 1951).

early as 1906 and was used for industrial fuel. Although indications of gas were observed, a thorough investigation did not begin until the third Five-Year Plan. Discovery of rich gas deposits near the village of Yelshanka, about 15 miles from Saratov, took place in August 1942. The gas erupted from the gas-bearing strata at extremely high pressure. A 16-mile pipeline was built immediately from Yelshanka to Saratov to carry gas to the Saratov power plant.

The gas deposits north of Saratov were expanded and production increased so as to make it possible to supply at least a part of the needs of the city of Moscow for gas for lighting, heating, and cooking.

Gas fields: The gas fields stretch over an area of about 43 square miles on both sides of the Volga. They are the fields of Yelshanka, Teplovka, Kurdyum, and Dergachi.

Pipelines: A small pipeline connects Yelshanka and Saratov.[19] This pipeline was built in 1942 and 1943 and was a pattern for the construction of the big 528-mile, 12-inch gas pipeline to connect the Saratov fields with Moscow. Construction on the latter was started in 1944 and it was put into operation in August 1947.[20] It crosses at least 40 highways and 80 rivers and lakes on its way to Moscow. Throughput capacity is 47.7 million cubic feet daily, or about 17.4 billion feet annually.

The Emba Region

South of the Second Baku, on the north coast of the Caspian Sea, lies the Emba oil region. In its vast expanse it resembles an acute triangle with the Caspian coast as its base and the city of Orsk, 440 miles to the north, as its apex. This tremendous size should not lead to an exaggeration of the significance of the Emba region. Although structures with promise of oil are known to exist throughout the area, commercial oil deposits, up to the present, seem to be concentrated in the coastal zone. The only two exceptions are the fields of Shubar-Kuduk and Dshaksymai. They lie about midway between Orsk and the coast and about 80 miles south of Aktyubinsk.

The Emba region was opened shortly before World War I and commercial production began in 1912. In 1916 its fields produced about 265,000 tons, with Makat and Dossor supplying the bulk. In

---

[19] Translator's note: A 17-mile, 16- to 18-inch pipeline.

[20] Translator's note: Such construction is almost routine in the United States. See Leeston, *op.cit.*, pp. 38ff., 56ff., and *Gas Age*, December 4, 1952, pp. 39f., 78f.

1938 production was in excess of 600,000 tons. For 1950 the fourth Five-Year Plan set a goal of 1,200,000 tons. This scheduled amount was exceeded by about 100,000 tons. The comparatively slow increase in production from 265,000 tons in 1916 to 1,300,000 tons in 1950, Leimbach thinks,[21] must be due to the poor water supply in this area. He rightly says, "The slow development of the Emba region in the desert steppe on the north coast of the Caspian Sea cannot be understood without considering the extremely critical water problem." No doubt further oil deposits will be discovered in the Emba region, for it has a great number of salt plugs on the flanks and crests of which oil frequently accumulates. But the development of such deposits will be limited by the poor water supply.[22]

Political division: The fields of the Emba region are administered by the Embaneft and Aktyubneft trusts under the Kazakhstanneft oil group.

Oil fields: In the coastal zone of the Caspian Sea, west of the Ural River, lie the oil fields of Novobogatinskoye and Chernaya-Retchka; south of the Emba River are the fields of Koschagyl and Kulsary; between the Emba and Ural Rivers are the fields of Iskininskiy, Dossor, Baychunas, Makat, and Sagiz; and about 220 miles east of this last group are the Shubar-Kuduk and Dshaksymai fields.

All the Emba fields lie on salt domes, in contrast to the fields in the Baku, Groznyy, and Maykop areas. A large number of salt plugs is typical of the Emba region. There is, on the average, a salt plug to each 186 square miles.

Oil processing: Four small refineries operate in the Emba region, at Guryev, Iskininskiy, Novobogatinskoye, and Orsk. The refinery at Orsk is by far the most important of the four. It has an annual throughput capacity of 1,400,000 tons, including a cracking capacity of 250,000 tons.[23]

Pipelines: The largest pipeline of the area is the 525-mile line[24]

---

[21] See Werner Leimbach, *Die Sowjetunion, Natur, Volk und Wirtschaft* (Stuttgart, 1950), p. 341.

[22] Translator's note: "According to official statement the major Emba Basin oil area of Kazakhstan has not met expectations. . . . The area did not reach its Five-Year Plan goal of about 9 million barrels in 1950, and work there was marked by poor utilization of modern techniques for increasing production." Associated Press report in the *New York Times*, March 3, 1952, p. 4, col. 6.

[23] Translator's note: The oil produced in the Emba region is high-grade crude oil, suitable for use as aviation gasoline and high-grade lubricating oil. See Leeston, *op.cit.*, p. 146.

[24] Translator's note: 12 inches in diameter.

FIG. 14. The western half of the Kazakh Soviet Socialist Republic,
including the Emba region.

Reproduced from Shabad, *Geography of the USSR* (New York: Columbia University Press, 1951).

from Guryev on the coast to Orsk, which began operating in 1936. Its purpose is to carry the crude oil produced on the coast to Orsk for refining; from there the finished products are shipped to the industrial regions on the other side of the Ural Mountains. In the 1930's three lines were built connecting other places with the Guryev-Orsk line. One connecting line went from Kulsary to Makat via Koschagyl, another from Baychunas to Iskininskiy, and the third from Rakusha on the Caspian Sea to Dossor.

The Ukhta-Pechora Area

In the northeastern corner of European Russia lies the oil and gas district of Ukhta-Pechora, the name of which is derived from the city of Ukhta and the Pechora River. This is the northernmost oil province of the Soviet Union. It centers around Ukhta. Some of the gas fields are remote from that city; for instance, the field of Cherdyn, which lies about 250 miles south of Ukhta. Indications of oil have been observed here since the time of Peter the Great. Production from these oil deposits was tried spasmodically in 1872, 1890, and 1905. At the beginning of the twentieth century four oil-producing wells had been drilled by the Yarega River. However, since quantities produced were small, production was abandoned. Soviet geologists directed attention to this area in the 1920's, proving that the subsoil of the region contained oil in commercially significant quantities, and drilling was resumed in the 1930's. This oil has an extraordinarily high pour point and freezes at comparatively high temperatures. It is produced by mining, which is unusual in the industry. Production surpassed 100,000 tons in 1937 and reached 200,000 tons in 1940. During World War II, when oil became scarce in Russia on account of deficient production in the southern fields, production in Ukhta-Pechora was increased quickly and wastefully to more than 1,200,000 tons. It can be assumed that with the end of the political and military emergencies of those years the rate of production has been reduced to a normal, efficient rate. For 1950 production is estimated at 800,000 tons, which is of considerable importance in supplying the northeastern part of European Russia.

As important as oil production, and perhaps more so, is the production from natural-gas fields in this area. From the award in 1947 of the Stalin Prize for their discovery, some authors infer, not without justification, that the emphasis in the Ukhta-Pechora area is on gas

[97]

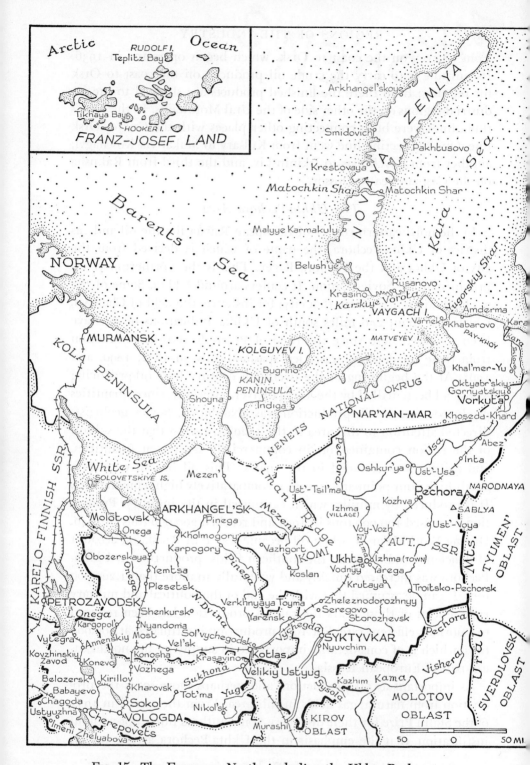

FIG. 15. The European North, including the Ukhta-Pechora area.

Reproduced from Shabad, *Geography of the USSR* (New York: Columbia University Press, 1951).

rather than oil production.[25] This assumption is confirmed in a way by the construction of a large gas pipeline from the gas field of Izhma via Molotov to Izhevsk. The construction of a pipeline 500 miles long has as a prerequisite the need for a sufficient supply of natural gas over a long period of time.

Political division: The oil area of Ukhta-Pechora is a closed territory where only forced laborers and exiles are employed. It is, therefore, subject neither to an oil group nor to an independent trust, but to a special administration.

Oil fields: In the immediate neighborhood of Ukhta lie the oil fields of Yarega and Chibien, while the Ust-Kulom field is south of Ukhta. The gas field of Izhma lies southeast of Ukhta and is the point of origin of the gas pipeline to Izhevsk. The gas field of Cherdyn lies midway between Ukhta and Molotov on the pipeline. All these fields are on anticlines.

Oil processing: The only refinery in the area is located in Ukhta. However, it is only a topping plant; that is, the lighter fractions of crude oil, gasoline, kerosene, and diesel oil are produced, while the processing of the residue is done in other refineries.

Pipelines: A gas pipeline 500 miles long has been laid from Izhma via Molotov to Izhevsk. To transport the oil and coal produced in the Pechora area (which is also very rich in coal), the great Pechora railroad was built between 1942 and 1948.[26] This railroad branches off at Kotlas, and runs via Ukhta to Amderma on the Arctic Ocean. It connects Moscow with the Barents Sea and is of great significance in the transportation of petroleum.

The Central Asiatic Oil Aea

In the Soviet republics of Uzbekistan, Tadzhikistan, and Kirghizstan, east of Turkmenistan, are located three oil fields of varying significance. The most important is the Fergana Valley field which stretches across the entire Fergana Basin. Small quantities of oil were produced in this field for many decades. This production came from various small areas. Today, after systematic exploration of the area, which is rich in raw materials, 21 fields produce oil and gas.

25 See Leimbach, *op.cit.*, p. 346.

26 Translator's note: All of this was accomplished with the help of forced or slave labor, and resulted in the death of thousands of people in the icy cold of that region. On this basis a gigantic construction program is projected and is being carried out. It includes railroads, canals, power plants, etc.

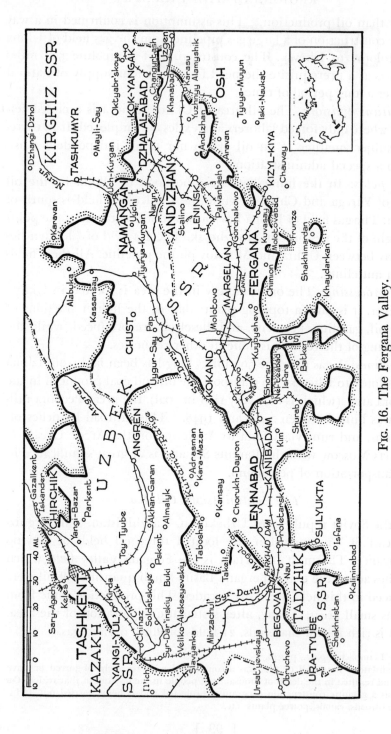

FIG. 16. The Fergana Valley.

Reproduced from Shabad, *Geography of the USSR* (New York: Columbia University Press, 1951).

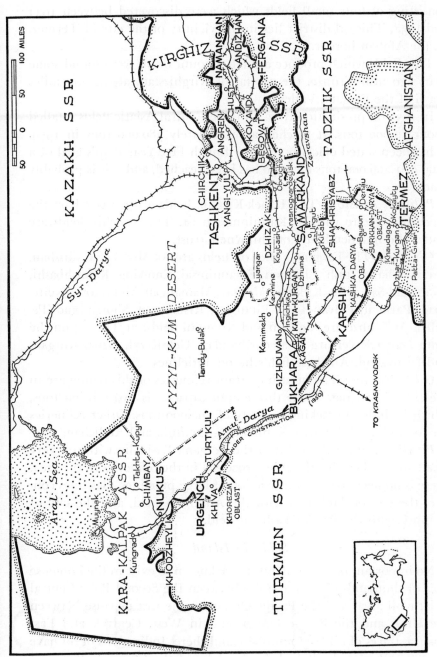

Fig. 17. The Uzbek Soviet Socialist Republic.

Reproduced from Shabad, *Geography of the USSR* (New York: Columbia University Press, 1951).

About 250 miles south of the Fergana Valley lies a small oil district, consisting of four small fields which were discovered between 1934 and 1938. This oil district lies in the vicinity of the city of Termez, on the Afghan border.

Two fields which produce a small amount of oil were found some years ago near Frunze, the capital of Kirghizstan, about 200 miles north of the Fergana Valley.

In 1933 oil production from all these Central Asiatic fields totalled about 50,000 tons. It reached approximately 380,000 tons in 1939. It has been stated officially that the fourth Five-Year Plan's goal of a total of 1,206,000 tons for 1950 has been reached, and this is probably true.

Political division: The Uzbek-Kirghiz fields are managed by the Sredasneft group with its Kalininneft trust. The Tadzhik fields are under the independent Voroshilovneft trust.

Oil fields: The Fergana Valley oil fields are Ak-Mecket, Andinzhan, Barzik, Changyrtash, Chimion, Encumimsai, Eno-Sing, Kamishbashi, Kyanabad-Sah, Kim, Kulmen, Malisay, Mamangan, Melnikovo, Nefte-abad, Parkent, Palvan-Tash, Pitaussay, Ristananto, Shorsu, and Te-kebel. At Frunze are the Chu and Komosol fields; at Termez on the Amu Darya River are located Khaudag, Uch-Kyzyl, Dzhar-Kurgan, and Kirovabad. All these fields lie on anticlines.

Oil processing: The most important refineries of this region are in the city of Fergana. Their throughput capacity is two million tons, which includes a cracking capacity of 500,000 tons. Other refineries are located in Melnikovo, Kanibadam, Leninsk, and Andizhan.

Pipelines: Since the fields of the Fergana Basin lie within a very small area and crude oil can be processed in the refineries in the area, there is no need for the construction of large pipelines. Gas lines connect the city of Andizhan with the Andizhan field, and the city of Leninsk with the Palvan-Tash gas field.

Sakhalin Island

No important oil or gas deposits are known to exist in the immense area of thousands of square miles between the Second Baku-Central Asiatic oil areas and the Pacific Ocean. In the vast expanse between the Urals and the Pacific Ocean, and in West, Central, and East Siberia, traces of oil are found here and there. Indications of oil have been found on Lake Baikal, in the delta of the Chatanga River, at Ust-Maya, and on the Kamchatka Peninsula. So far, however, commercially productive oil fields have not been discovered in these regions. The only oil deposit being explored in the vast area between the Urals and the Pacific Ocean is on Sakhalin Island, 3,000 miles distant from the Fergana Valley and the Second Baku.

As a result of the Russo-Japanese War in 1905, Russia lost the southern half of the island to Japan. After World War I, the Japanese leased portions of the northern part of the Island kept by the Russians in an attempt to improve their oil supply. Production began on a small scale in 1921 but increased constantly thereafter. This favorable development aroused the Soviet government and it began an active exploration of the area. It forced a checkerboard partition of the fields between Japan and the Soviet Union, whereby the Japanese concessions were surrounded by Russian fields. The Soviet Union carried on intensive exploration and drilling operations. They were so successful that Soviet production surpassed Japanese production on Sakhalin from 1935 on. At the end of World War II Japan lost all of her concession in North Sakhalin, and also lost South Sakhalin, where oil deposits had been discovered. At present the Soviet Union owns all of Sakhalin and its oil deposits, and controls production.

The following table shows the development of oil production on the Island.[27]

TABLE 28. Sakhalin Crude-Oil Production
(tons)

1921	295	1936	472,000
1922	1,030	1937	508,000
1923	1,324	1938	562,000
1924	11,765	1939	588,000
1925	12,794	1940	588,000
1926	26,618	1941	588,000
1927	64,706	1942	588,000
1928	99,559	1943	735,000
1929	166,765	1944	735,000
1930	265,441	1945	882,000
1931	402,058	1946	882,000
1932	386,911	1947	1,030,000
1933	343,823	1948	845,000
1934	423,676	1949	1,000,000
1935	374,264	1950	1,200,000

27 Translator's note: "The petroleum fields are producing some of the best grade fuel of the USSR," according to Theodore Shabad, *Geography of the USSR* (New York, 1951), p. 332.

FIG. 18. Sakhalin Island.

Reproduced from Shabad, *Geography of the USSR*
(New York: Columbia University Press, 1951).

Present production is estimated at 1.2 million tons. The importance of this production for the Soviet Union can hardly be exaggerated. In the first place, it serves as the oil supply of the army in the Far East, of the Far Eastern industrial district on the Amur River, and of coastal and ocean navigation in the Pacific. Without the oil from Sakhalin the army, industry, and shipping would depend upon imports of crude oil and oil products from overseas or from European Russia. In this case shipments would have to travel a distance of 4,400 to 5,000 miles over the Trans-Siberian Railroad.

Political division: The Sakhalin oil fields are under the independent Sakhalinneft trust.

Oil fields: The most important oil fields on Sakhalin Island lie north of the fortieth parallel. Less productive fields are located in the southern part of the Island. The northernmost field is Okha, near the city of the same name. Immediately south of it is Ekhabi, and farther south are Poronay, Nutovo, Vigrek, and Katangli. All these fields are on anticlines.

Oil processing: The Island has only two refineries, at Okha and Moskalvo. Four more refineries are located on the continent, at Nikolayevsk, Komsomolsk, Khabarovsk, and Vladivostok. The refineries of Nikolayevsk, Komsomolsk, and Khabarovsk have an annual crude-oil-refining capacity of 225,000 tons each, and a cracking capacity of 75,000 tons each.

Pipelines: A pipeline, which was built in several stages from 1937 on, connects the Ekhabi field with Okha and Okha with Nikolayevsk on the continent, then runs along the Amur River via Komsomolsk to Khabarovsk. This pipeline carries Sakhalin crude oil directly to the industrial area of the Far East.

PART IV

PROBLEMS OF THE RUSSIAN OIL INDUSTRY

PROBLEMS OF THE RUSSIAN
OIL INDUSTRY

THE entire world oil industry is concerned today with the question of whether production can keep pace with the rapidly increasing demand for oil. The vital position, ever increasing in importance, which oil has assumed in the modern mechanized world, casts a shadow of tension over the world economy. The Soviet economy is also dominated by this problem. Could Russian oil production cover Russian demand, the Soviet Union would be self-sufficient, a condition essential to the stability of her economic system. If, however, demand exceeds production by a large amount, the Soviet Union would be dependent upon imports of large quantities of oil and oil products to guarantee her economic life. The weight of these truths influences the direction of her economic and foreign policies.

The treatment of this problem, which pushes itself into the foreground in any appraisal of the strength of the Soviet Union, suffers from bias. Considering the Soviet oil industry exclusively from a Russian point of view, it is easy to arrive at an overestimate because of the great development during the last 30 years and the strong position the industry occupies in the Russian economy today. If you contrast the Russian oil industry with the world oil industry or the American oil industry, you can easily make the mistake of underestimating, because you come to comparisons which should not be made because of the entirely different Russian conditions. To judge the problem correctly it is necessary to consider the Soviet oil industry both as a part of the Soviet economy and as a part of the world oil industry, and to correlate it with both. The following discussions compare, therefore, the accomplishments and tendencies of the Soviet oil industry with the achievements and directions of the American oil industry, its great antagonist, and the achievements and directions of the world oil industry.

THE OIL DEMAND OF THE SOVIET UNION

An examination of the Soviet oil situation today generally reaches the conclusion that the Russian oil supply is the Achilles' heel of the Soviet economy. This conclusion is drawn from a comparison of Russian production with the production of other countries, especially the

[109]

United States. But do they really have the same requirements? Is it permissible to compare the demand for oil in the Soviet Union with the demand of other countries, without considering the special factors which increase or diminish it here or there? What factors determine the demand for oil in the Soviet Union? In case Soviet oil production is insufficient, can demand be curtailed without impairing the Russian economy as a whole? These are the most important problems involved in the Russian demand for oil.

Can the Oil Demand of the Soviet Union Be Compared with the Oil Demands of Other Countries?

The sources of the world's supply of energy have changed basically during the last 30 years. Whereas, up to the First World War, the energy supply of most nations was exclusively based on coal, that mineral has lost its once-undisputed key position in the world's energy supply. Crude oil and natural gas have come to the fore as energy sources of equal importance. This tremendous shift, which has transformed the structure of the world economy, is shown in Table 29.

TABLE 29. Contributions of the Most Important Sources to the World Energy Supply, in Percentages of the Total[1]

Source of Energy	1920	1938	1949
Coal	83.5	65.4	50.6
Crude oil and natural gasoline	11.6	24.1	32.2
Natural gas	2.7	5.9	10.9
Water power (electricity)	2.2	4.6	6.3
Total	100.0	100.0	100.0

In the United States, which is not only the world's greatest producer of oil but also the greatest consumer, the percentage share of crude oil and gas is even higher. Both oil and gas contribute almost twice as much as coal to the energy supply. The triumphant march of the motor, which plays a predominant role in the United States, appears impressively in these figures.

While oil was used 50 years ago chiefly for lighting and lubricating, today it has assumed a dominant importance as a source of energy and heat. Modern transportation, an industrialized economy, mechanized agriculture—in fact, our entire public and private life—could not be imagined without petroleum.

[1] *Erdöl und Kohle*, III (1950), 639.

Industry and transportation, agriculture and household, and, not least, the armed forces of the land, sea, and air—all need gasoline, diesel fuel, lubricating oil, fuel oil, and the thousands of other petroleum products of our time. The statement is justified today that the increasing demand for oil products has become a sure sign or yardstick of the degree of civilization.

TABLE 30. Contributions of the Most Important Sources to the Energy Supply of the United States, in Percentages of the Total[2]

Source of Energy	1920	1938	1949
Coal	77.7	42.6	33.5
Crude oil and natural gasoline	15.4	39.1	39.4
Natural gas	5.7	15.0	23.1
Water power (electricity)	1.2	3.3	4.0
Total	100.0	100.0	100.0

The world as a whole, until now, could satisfy continually growing petroleum requirements through constantly increasing production. The potential demand of the world for oil products today, however, is substantially higher than the present actual consumption. Several countries still curtail consumption for economic, financial, or political reasons. If these restrictions are removed, a further heavy increase in oil demand must be expected. This discrepancy between potential demand and actual consumption is a decisive incentive toward expansion of production. It is this incentive that explains the huge rise in production which in the last 50 years has almost doubled from decade to decade. This gap involves a specific oil problem which is not present in the world economy of other raw materials; for instance, coal.

A comparison of world oil production, American production, and Soviet production reveals that Soviet oil production did not rise as rapidly as production in the world or in America. While world production increased about twelvefold and American production about tenfold between 1910 and 1950, Soviet production increased only fourfold during the same period.[3]

[2] *ibid.*, p. 638. (Translator's note: See also Erich W. Zimmermann, *World Resources and Industries* [New York, 1951], p. 454.)

[3] Translator's note: "Last year's [1951] industrial production [in Soviet Russia] went up by 16 per cent, which it is claimed raised it to a level twice as high as in 1940, and over three times that at the end of the war. The annual increase in the five preceding years amounted to 20 per cent or more, but the 1951 increase, measured in absolute

TABLE 31. Production of Oil in the World, the United States, and the
USSR between 1910 and 1950
(thousands of tons)

Year	World	United States	USSR
1910	45,109	28,315	9,680
1920	94,809	59,847	3,500
1930	194,060	121,336	17,545
1940	295,174	182,842	30,673
1950	522,840	270,000	37,600

A comparison of Russia's oil production and its development of
general industrial production clearly shows the lag in oil production.
World industrial production was about two and one-half times as
large in 1950 as in 1910, and American industrial production about
three and one-half times as large. The increase in oil production both
in the world and the United States was many times the increase in
industrial production. In the Soviet Union, however, the opposite is
observed. There industrial production was fourteen times as great
but oil production only four times as great.[4]

terms, was at least as large as ever before. The main effort has always been directed
to the heavy industries; the increase in the engineering industries between 1940 and
1951 amounted to no less than 178 per cent, but for the main consumer goods industries was only of the order of 30 to 40 per cent. Agricultural output has lagged
behind and last year [1951] suffered from bad weather. Grain production last year
totalled only 121 million metric tons, compared with 119 million tons in 1940 and 124
million in 1950." *Petroleum Press Service*, March 1952, p. 97. And on p. 97 of the same
issue: "Nevertheless, [petroleum] output has doubled since 1946 and is now rising by
28-35 million barrels a year."

Russian Production of Energy
(From *ibid.*, p. 97. One ton = 7 barrels)

	Crude Oil	Coal and Lignite	Electricity
	(millions of metric tons)		(billions of kilowatts)
1940	31.0	166.0	48.3
1946	21.6	162.0	49.5
1949	33.2	234.0	78.0
1950	37.9	260.0	90.0
1951	42.4	281.0	102.5
Per-cent increase, 1940-1951	37.0	69.0	112.0
Per-cent increase, 1946-1951	96.0	73.0	107.0

To the extent that electricity is coal-generated, coal output reappears in the righthand
column. All figures are computed from indications given in official Russian announce-
ments. The new hydroelectric power stations now being built on the Volga, Don, and
Dnieper Rivers, and on the Turkmen Canal will raise electrical production by about
22.5 billion kilowatts a year or by more than one fifth of last year's output. *ibid.*

[4] See Dr. W. v. Golovatcheff, "Stand der Weltindustrie," *Die Welt*, 1950, No. 304.

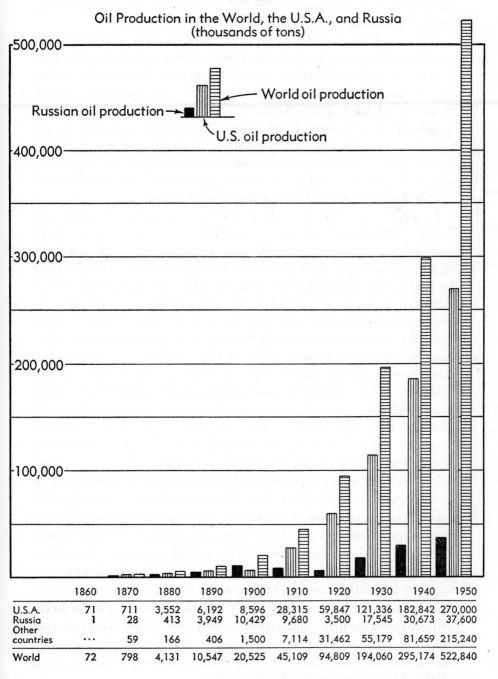

Fig. 19.

Oil Production in the World, the U.S.A., and Russia
(thousands of tons)

	1860	1870	1880	1890	1900	1910	1920	1930	1940	1950
U.S.A.	71	711	3,552	6,192	8,596	28,315	59,847	121,336	182,842	270,000
Russia	1	28	413	3,949	10,429	9,680	3,500	17,545	30,673	37,600
Other countries	...	59	166	406	1,500	7,114	31,462	55,179	81,659	215,240
World	72	798	4,131	10,547	20,525	45,109	94,809	194,060	295,174	522,840

Russian oil production did not keep pace with the development of world oil production or with the development of Russian industrial production.

This fact leads us to ask whether the Soviet Union is lacking in the conditions necessary for increased production, or whether the Russian economy did not make the same demands on the oil industry that the world economy made on the world oil industry. Since it is difficult to believe that the Soviet Union, with its extraordinary economic drive, neglected the important field of the oil industry, the problem is clarified by an examination of whether or not the Soviet Union gives preference to other sources of energy, such as coal and electricity. This should make understandable the low requirements of the Russian economy on the Russian oil industry.

Indeed, the fact that Russian coal production was nine times greater in 1950 than in 1910 (about 261 million tons, as compared with 28 million tons) shows that the Russian economy uses coal to a large degree in satisfying its demands for energy. The scheduled increase in coal production to 500 millions tons by 1960 shows that energy demands in the future are to be covered in the same proportion by the huge coal deposits. In addition, the tremendous energy production of power plants, especially hydroelectric plants, must be taken into consideration. Consumption of electricity was about forty-five times greater in 1950 than in 1910, increasing from two billion kilowatt-hours to about ninety billion kilowatt-hours. Electricity will be used to an exceptional degree in the future, as can be seen from the plans for the construction of giant power plants on the Volga River. Work on them has already commenced. According to two decrees of the Soviet government, dated August 21 and 31, 1950, power plants are to be built at Kuybyshev and Stalingrad, each of which will be able to generate ten billion kilowatt-hours of energy annually.[5] According to official Russian statements, these two power plants are to relieve the burden on oil. There is no doubt that already the Soviet Union satisfies with coal or electricity a large part of the energy requirements which in other countries are satisfied by petroleum.

Apart from these aspects, the question should be asked, Does the Russian economy, due to its entirely different structure, make lower requirements on its oil industry than other countries? This question

[5] See E. Thiel, "Die Elektrifizierung der Sowjetunion," *Zeitschrift fuer Raumforschung*, 1950, p. 176; also, "Riesenkraftwerke an der Wolga," *Frankfurter Allgemeine Zeitung* (Frankfort on the Main—Trans.), October 13, 1950.

must be answered in the affirmative. In this connection it is interesting to note that the United States in the first six months of 1950 consumed daily a minimum of 360,000 tons of gasoline out of a daily average consumption of about 850,000 tons of oil products.[6] This high gasoline consumption in the United States is understandable, since out of a total of about 61,000,000 motor vehicles operated in 1949 throughout the world, including the Soviet Union (the world total, including that of the Soviet Union, was 59,464,000 motor vehicles on January 1, 1950),[7] a minimum of 43,430,000 vehicles were operated in the United States; whereas, there may not be more than 2,000,000 motor vehicles operated in the Soviet Union.[8] Such structural differences in the two economies make themselves felt in the petroleum industry. In the United States, where one person out of three has an automobile, oil consumption serves a scale of living far in excess of the normal living standard. Such a scale of living is not found in the Soviet Union; thus, the Russian oil industry is not burdened with such requirements.[9]

One arrives easily at wrong conclusions in comparing indiscriminately the increase in world oil production and demand with the performance and achievements of the Russian oil industry and the demand for its products, without regard for the special economic, political, and sociological conditions in the Soviet Union.

What Factors Determine the Russian Oil Demand?

The factors that determine the oil demand of a given economy are basically the same in all countries; the only difference is the weight laid upon the various factors in each case. The most important factors are the size of the economic unit, the population, the technological status of the country, and, finally, the dynamic policy pursued by the economic system.

[6] See *Erdöl und Kohle*, III (1950), 523.

[7] See *ibid.*, p. 469.

[8] Dr. Gustav Egloff, in his address, "Strategic Oil Supplies," given at the convention of the American Petroleum Institute in Los Angeles on November 14, 1950, estimates the number of Soviet motor vehicles at 1,250,000. (Translator's note: See the *Petroleum Engineer*, Reference Annual, 1951, for Dr. Egloff's address.)

[9] See also the article "Contrasts: East and West," *Petroleum Press Service*, January 1951, pp. 1ff., where it says: ". . . the virtual absence of pleasure motoring in the U.S.S.R. and Eastern Europe means that any cut in consumption would immediately affect essential production and transport. Nearly half the oil consumption in the U.S.A. is for road vehicles; indeed the social and economic structure of the country is largely built around the motor car and motor truck. . . . In the U.S.S.R. roads and road transport are still relatively undeveloped."

Size of the territory: The size of the territory in itself is not necessarily a decisive factor. In some large countries, like India, the demand for oil is comparatively small. On the other hand, some countries with a small area, like Great Britain, have an extremely high demand for oil. However, the element of space is especially important in the case of a technically highly developed economy with a large territory.

In czarist Russia the vastness of the area had little bearing on the demand for oil. Industry then was limited to a few localities and the balance of the overwhelmingly agrarian country did not make any considerable demands on the oil industry. Territory became a determining factor only when the whole country was placed on a higher level of civilization. From then on, space made increasing demands for oil. Aside from transportation, with its obvious importance in such a large area, this factor of space gained special significance in the situation of industry, agriculture, and the armed forces in Russia.

Small countries are compelled to concentrate industry. In the Soviet Union, on the other hand, the vastness of the territory favors the tendency to decentralize industry. The ten regions of heavy industry, which form the backbone of the Russian economy, are separated in some cases by thousands of miles. What a challenge to the Soviet oil industry is this fact alone! It is not only necessary to supply oil to these areas, with vast distances separating them, but also to guarantee stability of the oil supply by maintaining sufficient storage.

Agriculture: Agriculture faces similar problems. In czarist times the chief farming area was concentrated on the steppes, which are favored in climate and vegetation.[10] To safeguard the food supply for a steadily increasing population, the Soviet government was forced to systematically make arable an area which had been cultivated theretofore little or not at all: the wooded steppe between the steppe zone on the north and the semi-desert steppe on the south. This development created "farming isles" in the newly opened lands, which face oil problems similar to those of industry as a whole, since farming is almost completely mechanized.

The Soviet army: The vast expanse of the Union raises the same problems for the army. Because of the extremely long frontiers, the Soviet government has divided the army into six independent army

[10] See Werner Leimbach, *Die Sowjetunion, Natur, Volk und Wirtschaft* (Stuttgart, 1950), p. 257.

groups with headquarters in these cities: Leningrad, Minsk, Odessa, Tbilisi, Tashkent, and Chabarovsk. Each of these army groups is organized to operate independently in an emergency. Therefore each of them has its own supply base and also its own oil supply. Increased oil storage is necessary to make an army group really independent.

All these considerations show that the oil demand of industry, agriculture, and the army in Russia cannot be judged by comparison with the total consumption of another country.

Population: Population itself is not a decisive factor in determining the oil requirements of a country. Therefore, care must be exercised in making comparisons based on population. For instance, Sweden with a population of about 7 million uses 3 to 4 million tons of oil products, and China with about 450 million people uses far less. However, generally speaking, population is an important factor in a comparison between two countries of about the same technical level. In the United States, for instance, where technology is an integral part of each individual's life, the population figure is necessarily a multiplier. In the Soviet Union, however, where the use of petroleum is artificially limited, the size of the population is less significant.

Urbanization: Much more important than its growth of population is the Soviet Union's consistent drive toward urbanization. The massing of the population in certain spots, which is a general characteristic of modern civilization, is intentionally and systematically sponsored by the Soviet government. This process, which concentrates the entire economic, political, and social life in the city, was begun as early as the first Five-Year Plan. The proportion of the urban population in the total population of the Soviet Union increased from 11.5 per cent in 1897 to 32.8 per cent in 1939.[11] In 1950 it may have reached 40 per cent. In the wake of this development, cities of medium size grew to metropolitan areas and many new cities reached a large size in a few years. The rapid tempo of this development is shown in Table 32.

In 1939 the Soviet Union had two cities with populations exceeding a million, nine cities with more than half a million people, and at least 70 cities with more than 100,000 people. Since then this trend has been accelerated. Urbanization in the Soviet Union is not, as in other countries, an accompaniment of industrialization. Lately it has been extended artificially to agriculture, by the establishment of pre-

[11] See *ibid.*, p. 218.

conceived "agrotowns." It is planned to do away with small towns, because they hamper farming on a large scale and the efficient use of manpower. They are to be replaced by agricultural economic centers, which gather in the entire population of the area and so gradually grow into "agrotowns."[12]

TABLE 32. Increase in Population of Some Russian Cities

City	1936	1939	1950
Moscow	2,030,000	4,140,000	5,050,000
Leningrad	1,690,000	3,190,000	3,300,000
Kiev	510,000	850,000	900,000
Baku	450,000	810,000	820,000
Novosibirsk	120,000	405,000	700,000
Kuybyshev	175,000	390,000	600,000
Saratov	220,000	375,000	600,000
Molotov	120,000	255,000	500,000
Karaganda	....	165,000	250,000

According to the opinion repeatedly voiced in petroleum literature, there is a close relationship between the demand for petroleum and the scale of economic well-being.[13] This is true also with regard to demand for petroleum and urbanization. The accumulation of masses of people in a small area leads to complicated forms of communal life and poses technical problems. Experience shows that solution of these problems involves increased petroleum requirements.

Technological progress: Even stronger and more enduring is the influence of the technological status of a country upon the demand for oil.

Czarist Russia entered the industrial age later than most of the European countries. Its industrial development lagged more than 50 years behind other capitalistic nations. To overcome this backward-

[12] In the Moscow region on January 1, 1950 there were only 6,069 *kolkhoz* (collective farms) and on July 1, 1950, only 1,668, according to *Bolshevik*, 1950, No. 12, p. 50. For the same period the number of *kolkhoz* in the Yaroslavl region dropped from 3,890 to 963, and in the White Russia Soviet Socialist Republic, from 9,771 to 3,279—*Pravda*, October 27, 1950 and November 14, 1950. See the basic article, "Organization and Establishment of the *Kolkhoz*," by N. W. Khrushchev, secretary of the Central Committee of the Soviet Union Communist Party, in *Pravda*, March 4, 1951. (Translator's note: This program now seems to be in abeyance. See *Petroleum Press Service*, March 1952, p. 98.)

[13] See J. E. Brantly, president of the Drilling and Exploration Company, in *Erdöl und Kohle*, III (1950), 199: "The high standard of living in the United States can easily be associated with the high oil consumption."

ness was the aim of the Five-Year Plans, which Stalin expressed in the words "catch up and surpass." With the initiation of the Five-Year Plans, which was the beginning of a general industrialization, collectivization, and motorization, a realization of the paramount significance of technology grew. "Technology decides everything," Stalin declared in 1931. The introduction of technological methods enabled the Soviet government to organize the huge territory of Russia into a centralized political body, to utilize the natural wealth of the country, and to develop new regions step by step. This development, of course, had a decided influence on the demand for petroleum in the Soviet Union. The demand was to increase year by year in the wake of this dynamic economic development.

The political element: The last factor is the political role a country plays willingly or is forced to play. The world political situation in which the Soviet Union has grown necessarily releases economic, political, and military energy that is strong and dynamic. An active power cannot forego a firm economic foundation. The Soviet government recognized this prerequisite. The transformation of the country from an agrarian state to an industrial state, the establishment of heavy industry, the adaptation of techniques, and the shaping of the state are steps necessary to taking and maintaining its world position.

Russia's annual oil requirements for traffic, agriculture, industry, and the armed forces exceed 40 million tons today, despite curtailment of civilian consumption. To keep pace with her rapid economic development, the Union plans to increase oil production to about 60 million tons by 1960, or by 1955 if possible. This figure reflects the Soviet estimate of the minimum annual requirement of their economy for the next ten years.[14]

Can the Soviet Oil Demand Be Curtailed without Injury to the Economy?

The total oil supply at the disposal of the Soviet Union in 1950 amounted to about 44 million tons. It was made up of the following (in millions of tons):

[14] Translator's note: "If this pace (of an annual increase of 28 to 35 million barrels at the present time) is maintained the target of 60 million metric tons, 400 to 450 million barrels, annually, originally set for 1960, may be reached by 1955, as has indeed been anticipated by the Russians some time ago." *Petroleum Press Service*, March 1952, p. 97.

Soviet production		39.0
Oil production	37.6	
Shale-oil production	0.4	
Synthetic-oil production	1.0	
Soviet imports		5.0
Oil imports	4.0	
Synthetic imports	1.0	
Total		44.0[15]

This total supply of oil and oil products, according to a careful estimate, may have been used as follows (also in millions of tons):

Soviet consumption		40.0
Industry	12.0	
Transportation	10.0	
Agriculture	9.0	
Households	1.0	
Soviet armed forces	8.0	
Soviet exports to China and Korea		4.0
Total		44.0

The basic questions are, Did this quantity meet the demand of the bulk consumers? and, if not, Can a discrepancy between the demand and the ability to fill the demand be eliminated in the future by a systematic curtailment of demand?

Industry: It can be assumed that the demands of Soviet industry, despite its rapid growth, have been met so far. Should the tempo of the development of Soviet industry continue, however, a sharp increase in oil demand must be anticipated. There is no doubt of this because the Eastern Bloc has a broad base of raw materials and an unsatisfied market. The Russian share of world industrial production has increased sixfold in the last 40 years, from 2.3 per cent in 1913 to 14.2 per cent in 1950, whereas the share of the United States in the industrial production increased only by one third for the same period, from 27.4 per cent in 1913 to 36.3 per cent in 1950.[16] Should this rise continue and Russian industry fail to meet energy demands from other sources, such as the giant power plants under construction, the question of a sufficient oil supply will become a serious problem.

[15] This total does not distinguish between crude oil and oil products, in order to facilitate an understanding of the statistics.
[16] See W. v. Golovatcheff, *op.cit.*

Aside from the development of industry generally, it is certain that the petrochemical industry, which has had a tremendous development in the United States, will be introduced in the Soviet Union also. The petrochemical industry can mass-produce products in which the Union is particularly interested; that is, synthetic rubber and other synthetics, alcohol, glycerin, ammonia, fertilizers, and explosives.[17] Artificial curtailment of the productivity of the Soviet Union because of a lack of petroleum would cause a lag in industrial development which would endanger its political role.

Motor traffic: Despite its notable progress, motor traffic in the Soviet Union does not play as important a role as in other highly industrialized countries, especially the United States. The 43 million motor vehicles in the United States in 1950 consumed more than one third of the total oil production of that country. The burden of motor traffic upon the Russian oil industry is not nearly so heavy. However, clearly noticeable today is a tendency to overcome the vastness of the land with a network of transportation connecting isolated regions with each other. The Soviet government could not stop the growth of this tendency, even if it desired. Any sharp reduction of the petroleum requirements of motor traffic therefore seems improbable, if not impossible, for a country like Russia.

Agriculture: In agriculture there are certain similarities between the Soviet Union and the United States because both countries have motorized farming operations, to a considerable extent, through wide use of tractors. The United States in 1950 had 3.5 million tractors in operation.[18]

While Soviet agriculture today does not employ such a great number of tractors, the schedules of the Five-Year Plans and the systematic mechanization of agriculture indicate that the Soviet government is endeavoring to speed up their use rather than to slow it down.[19] This fact is borne out by the official statement of the government that Russian agriculture in 1950 was allotted one-third more motor fuel than

17 See Dr. Gustav Egloff, "Chemikalien aus Erdöl im Jahre 1950 und im Jahre 2000," *Erdöl und Kohle,* III (1950), 417.

18 See *Erdöl und Kohle,* IV (1951), 103.

19 Translator's note: The latest available information is that adverse conditions are a strong deterrent, contrary to the intentions of the government. As *Petroleum Press Service,* March 1952, p. 98, points out, "there is at present a severe shortage of draught power in agriculture, which is responsible for heavy crop losses . . . the total draught power now available for agriculture is probably lower than in 1940 . . . at the beginning of 1951, Soviet agriculture employed 585,000 tractors (0.4 tractors per hectare [0.16 per acre] of sown area) and 13.7 million horses and mules. In 1938 they had 483,500 tractors (in the smaller prewar territory) and somewhat more in 1940."

in previous years. The almost complete mechanization of Russian farming would force a crisis and probably cause a disastrous food shortage in the event of an insufficient allotment of oil.

Despite many arguments pro and con there is no reason to believe that industry, transportation, or agriculture has been insufficiently supplied with oil. In the future the requirements of these large consumers may be satisfied if Russian oil production can be increased as scheduled to 60 million tons. However, the situation of the Soviet armed forces is different.

The armed forces: The Western World frequently says the Soviet armed forces are "supermotorized," and thinks their unusually high demands for oil could not be filled even in peacetime. This opinion is not correct. Out of 175 divisions which made up the Russian land force in 1950, only about 50 were motorized. Of course armed forces of the magnitude of the Soviet army, air force, and navy need a lot of oil for training and maintenance of their peacetime numbers. When, however, a quarter of the total oil production has been allotted to the Soviet armed forces, a considerable portion of it may have been used for storage. Under normal conditions—that is, when world peace is assured—a serious discrepancy between supply and demand does not exist for the Soviet armed forces. On the contrary, considerable reductions in demand may be possible. In an emergency, however, such conclusions would be thrown overboard.[20]

Conclusions: The following conclusions can be drawn from the facts mentioned above:

The oil demand of the Soviet Union cannot be compared absolutely with the demands of other countries on account of special conditions which do not permit a uniform approach.

The oil demand of the Soviet Union is dependent most of all upon the technological development of the nation and the role the Soviet Union has assumed in world politics.

An artificial restriction of Russia's oil demand is not possible without endangering its economic and political position.

THE SATISFACTION OF THE OIL DEMAND OF THE SOVIET UNION

Since the oil demands of the Soviet Union cannot be reduced, chief interest is centered on discovering how the steadily increasing de-

[20] Translator's note: See supra, p. 115, n. 9.

mands can be met. Is it possible for Russia to increase domestic oil production? What difficulties would such an increase have to overcome? Is the Soviet economic system an obstacle? Does Russia have sufficient reserves of oil? Is the steel supply assured? What are the prospects for Russian synthetics and for hydrogenation? Finally, on what imports can Russia count in the coming years? All these questions, which deal with the Soviet oil industry from different aspects, are interrelated. They must be answered.

Is Russian Oil Production Encouraged or Hampered by the Soviet Economic System?

The internationally recognized oil periodical, the *Oil and Gas Journal*, published in its December 21, 1950 issue a rather extensive article on the Russian oil industry. This article began with a short section entitled "Stalin's Achilles Heel," and concluded with the following remarks: "The Communist part of the world doesn't have much oil but our part, the democratic part,[21] has plenty.

"How come? Is Nature just mean to the commies? Or does a shortage of oil promote communism? Or does communism promote a shortage of oil?

"You're entitled to your own conclusion, but ours is No. 3. We claim that communism—or any form of government operation, for that matter—is incapable of finding much oil or building up much of an oil industry."[22]

The question "How come?" hits the core of the Russian oil problem. This question is the result of a statistical comparison of oil production in countries where the oil industry is nationalized and in countries where it is operated as a private enterprise. The oil industry is operated in most countries as a private enterprise. Exceptions are the USSR and the countries of the Eastern Bloc, in which Rumania, Hungary, and Albania are included; also, several countries in Central and South America, including Argentina, Brazil, Chile, Bolivia, and Uruguay.

In the Soviet Union and Argentina nationalization took place in 1920, Mexico and Bolivia nationalized their oil industries in 1938, and the countries of the Eastern Bloc followed suit after World War

[21] Translator's note: The author added the words "the democratic part," which are not in the original English-language article.
[22] The *Oil and Gas Journal*, December 21, 1950, p. 133.

II.[23] The degree of government control varies in these countries. Nationalization is most widely practiced in the Soviet Union where all private enterprise is eliminated.

A comparison of oil production in the most important countries where the oil industry is nationalized with the most important countries where the industry operates under a private enterprise system reveals an interesting picture.

TABLE 33. Development of Oil Production in Countries with
an Uncontrolled Oil Industry
(thousands of tons)

Year	U.S.A.	Venezuela	Iran
1930	121,336	20,074	6,547
1940	182,842	27,433	9,474
1950	270,000	78,000	31,800

TABLE 34. Development of Oil Production in Countries with
a State-Controlled Oil Industry
(thousands of tons)

Year	Soviet Union	Mexico	Argentina
1930	17,545	5,914	1,286
1940	30,673	6,450	2,936
1950	37,600	10,600	3,500

These figures are startling at first glance. It cannot be denied that the oil production of countries with a free economy rose more steeply between 1930 and 1950. Oil production in the United States more than doubled, it almost quadrupled in Venezuela, and it practically quintupled in Iran. On the other hand, oil production in countries where the industry is wholly or in part state-controlled also doubled, on the average, between 1930 and 1950, but did not participate in the big rise in oil production in countries with a free economy over the past decade. However, absolute production figures for countries with a socialized industry cannot be compared with those of the United States or Venezuela. Nevertheless, it certainly is a conspicuous fact that certain states which pursue a nationalistic oil policy—Brazil, Bolivia, and Chile—have to import oil and do not seem to have had great success in the development of their production.

23 Translator's note: As a result of their status as satellites of Soviet Russia.

This formal statistical view, however, does not lead to conclusive results. It is too readily subject to the fallacy of absolute figures and ignores special geological and economic factors in the several countries. A more critical investigation of these figures will lead to certain corrections.

It is not permissible to compare the Soviet oil industry with that of the South and Central American nations. For instance, there are considerable differences between the political and economic structures of the Soviet Union and Mexico. These differences are so strong that they do not permit the drawing of an analogy. Nor would a comparison of the Soviet, Venezuelan, and Iranian oil industries produce a correct picture. In neither Venezuela nor Iran has government influence been strong enough to build up, in its own right, an oil industry as significant as the Russian oil industry of today. Therefore, comparisons with Mexico, Argentina, Venezuela, and Iran do not produce a sound answer to the question of whether a nationalized or a free oil industry is preferable in the Soviet Union. The same holds true for Argentina. The only logical comparison is that of the United States and Soviet Russia, because the oil industry and general tendencies of economic policy in these two countries represent, at least to some degree, comparable quantities.

Now arises the basic question: Would the Soviet oil industry have produced more oil if it had been operated on a private, capitalistic basis? An answer to this difficult question can be arrived at only by considering the problem from various angles.

An outstanding characteristic of the oil industry is the fact that investment and operations are very costly. The oil industry requires an extremely high capital investment. Geological and geophysical exploration, drilling, production, construction of pipelines and tankers, erection of refineries and oil ports, storage, and, finally, costly scientific research in laboratories—all require such huge funds that the operators can only be large business concerns. They are the foundation of the oil industry. The tendency toward concentration—that is, the inclination to cooperate and merge which we observe in the oil industry—is the outgrowth of these high capital requirements and the unusual risk inherent in the oil industry. Such large economic units, the pillars of the oil industry, are found in the free economic system in the form of integrated companies, but in the system of a state-planned economy they take the form of syndicates or trusts.

The economic development of the United States put the oil industry into the hands of private companies operating under independent individuals, as it did all other fields of industry in the United States. The moment the United States oil industry began to develop, so much money was in private hands that the necessary funds were available and the young industry had no difficulty in finding sufficient capital. The situation in Russia was entirely different. At the end of World War I, Russia was still an agrarian country of the patriarchal type. Aside from the basic principles of the Soviet economic system, there was no opportunity for the rise of large private oil companies for both personal and financial reasons.[24] However, there were in czarist Russia private Russian oil companies; for instance, the Lianosov and Mantashev groups. These were part of a finance and holding company with strong English connections, the Russian General Oil Corporation. Since the lack of Russian private capital prevented the formation of larger Russian private companies, any government in Russia would have had to face the alternatives after World War I of granting exploration rights and production privileges to foreign companies or taking them into their own hands.

The big Anglo-American-Dutch oil companies were able, because of capital, technology, personnel, and organization, to build up an oil industry in Russia adequate in view of the geological possibilities. However, such a solution would have been contrary to Russian national pride, and therefore out of the question even if a free choice had been possible. Actually, a free choice was not possible because the Soviet ideology of economics negates a priori any capitalistic basis for private enterprise. Therefore it was natural for the oil industry to be taken over by the government.

In judging and evaluating the accomplishments of the Russian oil industry, the following facts should not be overlooked:

The hour of birth of the modern Soviet oil industry cannot be fixed earlier than the beginning of the state-planned economy; that is, in 1928. At that time the annual production of the United States exceeded the 100-million-ton mark. The Soviet oil industry was then in its very beginning, lacking sufficient equipment for scientific research and the support of a well-developed supply industry. Everything had to be newly begun in the Soviet Union: the training of geologists and

[24] Anton Zischka, *Asien, Hoffnung einer neuen Welt* (Oldenburg, 1950), p. 189: "Before 1914, Russia's textile industry was mainly German, her mining industry English and Belgian, the armament plants and transportation system chiefly French."

engineers, the development of research laboratories, the manufacture of drilling and production equipment, and the construction of modern refineries. In 1930, the first year in this statistical comparison, the United States had at her disposal trained scientific, technical, and managerial staffs with the necessary auxiliary forces. The Soviet Union had to build up this organization along with drilling and production operations. Many obvious shortcomings of the Russian oil industry have not been overcome at the present time; for instance, inadequate geological and geophysical exploration, backward testing techniques, little reworking of wells, and partly obsolete refining techniques. Only by considering the difficult situation of the Russian oil industry can the accomplishments of that industry be viewed in the right light.

Therefore, the opinion in the *Oil and Gas Journal* that the Soviet economic system is an obstacle to the development of the Russian oil industry is not entirely acceptable in its one-sided, black-and-white approach. While this economic system is hardly suited to European countries with their small territories and comparatively insignificant oil deposits, the Soviet Union, with its vast expanse and its economic projects which surpass the capital resources of private companies,[25] is inherently justified in using the system and has achieved a certain success with it. Unless the Soviet government is judged by the narrow criterion of production results, it cannot be denied that it developed great economic energies which gave the Russian oil industry a strong upward impulse.

Does the Soviet Union Have the Oil Reserves and the Personnel to Increase Production?

Stalin's demand for the increase of oil production by 1960 cannot be met unless the Soviet Union has sufficient available reserves and the ability to produce from them.

The first question is whether new commercial oil deposits can be found. As elsewhere, in the Soviet Union the hopes for the future of the domestic oil industry are based on the estimate of oil reserves; but this estimate is affected, as is everything having to do with the future, by a certain speculative trait. The problems of oil reserves are the uncertainty of their existence, the difficulty of discovering them,

---

25 Translator's note: Experience shows they do not surpass the financial strength and resources of private companies. See A. M. Leeston, *Magic Oil, Servant of the World* (Dallas, 1951), p. 20.

and doubt as to their profitableness. These troubles are shared by the Soviet industry with the oil industries in every other country. But in contrast to the United States and other countries which are thoroughly explored, these problems are aggravated in the Soviet Union by the large territory and the difficulty of surveying such a vast space. Therefore, predictions as to the location and size of Russian oil deposits can be made only with great caution. Even where it has been possible, by means of geological and geophysical methods, to pinpoint the locations of oil deposits, it is, for the time being, hardly possible to make exact estimates of their size. These uncertainties are the reason for the tremendous differences in the estimates of several oil experts. These discrepancies are enhanced by the fact that statements of estimates are not always made according to the methods of exact science. Frequently, economic and political tendencies influence the individual point of view and lead to an over- or underestimation.

To what large differences these circumstances can lead is shown by a comparison of statements about, and estimates of, Russian oil reserves. Soviet oil scientists estimated that on January 1, 1938 oil reserves in the Soviet Union were 8.64 billion tons, or about 55 per cent of the total world oil reserves. G. M. Lees, chief geologist of the Anglo-Iranian Oil Company, estimates the total oil reserves of the Soviet Union at 14 billion tons.[26] The well-known American oil scientist, Dr. Gustav Egloff, arrives at a higher figure. He fixes the Russian oil reserves at 20 billion tons, or 25 per cent of the world reserves, which he puts at 80 billion tons.[27]

All these not-very-precise estimates have only limited value for practical purposes. Only too frequently they change artificially stimulated hopes into bitter disappointments. The Russian economic leaders, realizing very well the value of, but also the problem involved in, oil reserves, sought to simplify the problem by working out a clear system of classification by which all mineral deposits are grouped. Certainly all other oil countries apply such classifications as "proved," "probable," and "potential." The Russian classification is distinguished, however, by the fact that from the groupings are drawn immediate conclusions for economic utilization. The Soviet Union follows a practice of translating theoretical findings on oil reserves into practical, measurable quantities. (See the list of classifications in the appendix.)

[26] See *Erdöl und Kohle*, III (1950), 627.
[27] See Egloff, "Strategic Oil Supplies," *op.cit.*

Considering the points of view of the several estimators, it would not be incorrect to estimate the *proved* reserves of the Soviet Union at the present time at a minimum of one billion tons. Thanks to the development of modern scientific methods, which ascertain oil reserves more accurately every year, new discoveries can be expected in a huge territory which has been explored but little by geologists and geophysicists, but which offers, according to a summary judgment, conditions for large oil deposits. Thus there is little doubt that the Soviet industry has a firm foundation which assures it a future high-ranking position in the world oil industry.

The exploitation of these considerable possibilities depends not only upon the availability of funds, which is a serious problem in the Soviet Union, but also on the ability of the personnel of the oil industry; that is, on their technical training in discovering and developing, and in producing from, the reserves. In this respect the Soviet oil industry has deficiencies the elimination of which will take years. Despite great efforts, there is no doubt that Russian petroleum science and technology are far inferior to American. For instance, like most other oil countries, Russia is not yet able to manufacture roller bits which are the equal of the high-quality American rock bits. The isolation of the Soviet industry and the consequent lack of exchange of personnel and experience with the United States are felt. The successful solution of the problem of training a large number of highly qualified petroleum technicians, scientists, and economists will be instrumental if Russia increases its domestic production.[28]

Is the Steel Supply of the Russian Oil Industry Assured?

One of the most critical problems of every oil industry is securing sufficient steel for production and refining (i.e., for drilling pipe, pipelines, and refineries) and for transportation and distribution (i.e., for tankers, pipelines, and storage facilities). Though the United States, with a production of 97 million tons in 1950, was by far the world's largest steel producer, even the American oil industry had some difficulty with steel. The Steel Committee of the National Petroleum Council estimated a demand for steel in 1950 of about 8.5

[28] Translator's note: "On its upper level Russian technology is excellent. . . . Below this level, however, is a vacuum which shows in a shortage of such classifications as skilled mechanics, welders and unit operators." Dahl M. Duff, "Refining in Russia," *Oil and Gas Journal*, March 17, 1952, p. 181.

million tons for the entire domestic petroleum industry. Steel requirements were distributed as follows:[29]

TABLE 35. Steel Demand of the American Oil Industry in 1950

Purpose	Quantity (millions of tons)	Percentage of total
Production	2.8	33
Transportation	1.4	17
Refining	0.5	6
Distribution	1.8	21
Natural-gas pipelines	2.0	23
Total	8.5	100

With an oil production of 270 million tons and a demand for steel of 8.5 million tons, there was an average in 1950 of one ton of steel used per thirty-two tons of oil produced. One twelfth of the total American steel production had to be set aside for the various purposes of the oil industry.

These ratios do not apply in all oil regions of the world. In the United States, the oil industry, with 33 per cent of the steel demand, occupies first place as a steel user. This is understandable, since oil production in 1950 came from no less than 450,000 producing wells. For 1951, it is planned to drill 43,400 wells for a total footage drilled of 160 million feet.[30] On the other hand, production in the Middle East in 1950 was about 86 million tons from only 200 wells which required comparatively small quantities of steel. Such differences occur in transportation, refining, and distribution, as well as in production.[31] Therefore, it is difficult to compare the American steel re-

[29] See *Erdöl und Kohle*, III (1950), 637.

[30] See *Erdöl und Kohle*, III (1950), 637. (Translator's note: 44,826 wells, according to *World Oil*, Review-Forecast Issue, February 15, 1952.)

[31] How important such differences can be is shown by an article in the November 15, 1950 issue of *Focus*, a magazine published by the American Geographical Society. This article compares transportation in the American and Russian oil industries. According to it, shipments of oil were made as follows:

	U.S.A. in 1946 (per cent)	Soviet Union in last available year, probably 1938 (per cent)
By water	19	46
By rail	2	43
By pipeline	79	11

quirements in tons with the steel needs in tons of the Russian oil industry. However, the American figures afford certain bases because differences within the several categories compensate for each other, so that the steel demand per ton of oil can be compared with the same ratio for Russia.

Assuming that the Russian oil industry uses one ton of steel per 30 to 35 tons of oil, about 1.25 million tons of steel are used to produce about 39 million tons of oil, oil shale, and synthetics. The actual steel demand is probably higher, because the Soviet petroleum industry is expanding at present. However, it should not exceed 2 million tons at the maximum. With a Russian steel production of about 27 million tons in 1950, the requirement of the oil industry should have been less than one twelfth of that amount.

This steel demand appears very high for Russian ideas because the rapid industrialization places a strong demand upon the steel supply for other industries, also. Without doubt, the steel supply of the Russian oil industry is a serious bottleneck. Apart from being evident in many other factors, this is shown by the fact that the Soviet Union is vitally interested in the importation of seamless Mannesmann tubes, which are used chiefly in oil, shale, and gas production.[32]

Definitely, a future increase in oil production according to Stalin's demand will be possible only if steel production increases proportionately.

Can Synthetic-Oil Production Make a Substantial Contribution to the Russian Oil Supply?

Should motor fuel become scarce in the Russian economy because of increasing motorization and insufficient cracking capacity, the question of whether the gap in supply could be closed by production of synthetic motor fuel would become acute. Synthetic motor fuel is more expensive to produce than motor fuel made from crude oil and economically cannot compete with the latter. But political situations could arise in which the question of economy would recede behind the need for a sufficient supply of motor fuel. This is particularly true in a planned economic system like the Russian, where production comes first, instead of considerations of private profit.

However, there may be a difference in the way profit is judged in the Soviet Union, as contrasted with other countries, because the unity

[32] See "Engpässe der sowjetrussischen Industrie," *Neue Züricher Zeitung*, February 2, 1951.

of its industry compensates for the profit factor. For instance, the exclusive use of petroleum has made it necessary so far to supply the new industrial district on Lake Baykal with oil from the Second Baku. These huge shipments could be eliminated if efforts to use coal deposits on Lake Baykal in the production of synthetic motor fuel were successful. Even if such operations had not proved profitable from a strict economic standpoint, the elimination of the transportation over long distances would compensate for certain costs within the framework of the operation. Similar considerations would hold true for other industrial districts and for independent army groups.

The fact that the chemical composition of coal permits conversion into liquid motor fuel was first discovered in Germany. In 1913, Friedrich Bergius developed the so-called hydrogenation method, which was improved by Matthias Pier. This process liquefies coal by the addition of hydrogen at temperatures of 848°-1060° Fahrenheit. The first commercial plant to produce gasoline by hydrogenation was opened at Leuna in 1927. In the 1920's Franz Fischer and E. Tropsch followed with the synthesis process which permits manufacture not only of gasoline but also of valuable by-products for the chemical industry. This method completely vaporizes the coal, then the gaseous parts are converted into liquid hydrocarbons. In Germany both processes were so highly developed that the Germans operated no less than nine synthesis and fourteen hydrogenation plants during World War II. How important the contribution of these two production processes was is shown by the fact that in 1943 the German synthesis plants produced about 450,000 tons of motor fuel, and the hydrogenation factories about 3,350,000 tons.

Germany was not the only place where the importance of the synthesis and hydrogenation processes was recognized; strong interest was shown in India, South Africa, and the Far East. The processes were given serious consideration in the United States, also, but that country's rich domestic oil deposits and the possibility of satisfying unexpectedly increasing demand through imports from the Caribbean area made the development of a hydrogenation and synthesis industry unnecessary for the time being. In the Soviet Union, however, the problem has attracted increasing interest because the establishment of a hydrogenation and synthesis industry has become almost a necessity from many points of view. Motorization is making demands on the fuel supply to an extent that cannot be satisfied by oil production alone unless the requirements of the army should be diminished![33] Moreover, the Soviet Union has large coal deposits in Europe and Asia, such as the anthracite deposits around Lake Baykal, that are particularly suited for the synthesis and hydrogenation processes of oil manufacture. Finally, the Russian economic system with its tendency toward self-sufficiency is not particularly concerned with profitability, which is frequently an obstacle to the construction of hydrogenation and synthesis plants in countries with private enterprise systems. The large size of the country and the fact that all oil regions lie within the European portion of the nation, with the exception of those in Central Asia and on Sakhalin Island, compel the Russian government to consider the advantages of the establishment of synthetic-motor-fuel bases in the vicinity of remote consumption centers.

All these possibilities may be realized because the Russians found in the Eastern Zone of Germany more than 60 per cent of all the German synthesis and hydrogenation plants with qualified staffs. These plants were transferred in part to Soviet joint-stock companies and shipped to Russia. For instance, large sections of the Leuna and Poelitz plants were dismantled and rebuilt at Dzerzhinsk and Gorkiy, where they manufacture synthetic aviation gasoline from coal. In addition, two German plants have been rebuilt at Irkutsk on Lake Baykal.

The fourth Five-Year Plan scheduled for 1950 a synthetic-motor-fuel production of 900,000 tons. Even so, the Soviet Union does not yet have a synthetic-oil industry comparable to the highly technical and efficient former German synthetics industry. Present annual production in Russia is estimated at about one million tons. It is certain that the production of synthetic motor fuel from coal will gain tremendous importance in the Soviet Union as soon as it has passed through the stage of experimentation and overcome initial difficulties.

How Much of the Russian Oil Demand Can Be Covered by Imports?

Between 1927 and 1937 the Soviet Union was an important exporting country. With 1932 oil exports at about six million tons, she became engaged in a fierce struggle with the other oil countries for the world market. From 1937 on, her exports declined steadily and at present are insignificant, apart from occasional export ship-

[33] Translator's note: See the excellent article by George G. Rosu, "Synthetic Fuels in Eastern Germany, Czechoslovakia, Poland and Bulgaria," in the *Oil and Gas Journal*, June 30, 1952, pp. 447ff.

ments for political purposes. Today, on the contrary, the Soviet Union makes every effort to attract as much oil as possible through imports, and this seems to support the opinion that domestic production is barely sufficient.

The most important European countries from which Russia can import oil or synthetic oil are Rumania, Hungary, Albania, Czechoslovakia, Austria, and Eastern Germany. All these countries have the characteristic, and also the problem, that their relations with the Soviet Union are not just economic, but also include a large measure of political and ideological factors. The close political contact guarantees and strengthens the economic ties. On the other hand, there is a danger that the economic ties will loosen if other political influences should achieve importance in these countries.

Rumania: Among the countries which contribute to Russian oil supply, Rumania is first. It was one of the earliest, and is also among the most important, oil countries of the world. With a production of 4.3 million tons, it occupied twelfth place in 1950. Since Rumania needed for its purposes only a small part of its production, it has always played a large role as an exporter of oil. The Rumanian oil industry, in which foreign-capital investment has been prevalent, was subject to the troubled political conditions of the country and to various political and economic pressures which prevented continuity of operations and caused a great deal of waste. During World War II the Rumanian oil fields were controlled first by Germany and from 1944 by Soviet Russia. The foreign oil companies active in Rumania were finally expropriated in July 1948. Today, Rumanian oil production is exclusively managed by Russo-Rumanian state companies. How unfavorable an influence the lack of stable political and economic conditions is on production is shown in the following table:

TABLE 36. Development of Oil Production in Rumania[34]
(thousands of tons)

1936	8,700	1942	5,665	1948	4,000
1937	7,150	1943	5,273	1949	4,300
1938	6,594	1944	3,512	1950	4,300
1939	6,226	1945	4,690	1951	4,000[35]
1940	5,810	1946	4,237	1952	4,100[35]
1941	5,453	1947	3,809		

[34] *Erdöl und Kohle*, III (1950), 355.

While the *Welt*, in a special Rumanian report on January 15, 1951, estimated the Rumanian oil production in 1949 at approximately 3,000,000 tons and in 1950 at less

This table shows that Rumanian oil production declined rapidly from a peak of 8.7 million tons in 1936 and, despite all efforts in the postwar years, in 1950 was only half the 1936 production. The poor performance of the Rumanian oil industry is the direct result of the bad condition of drilling and other oil-field equipment, which dates from prewar years in large part. This lack has made itself even more felt since the United States and Great Britain were eliminated as suppliers of drilling and production equipment for political reasons. The Soviet Union with its large demands is only to a limited extent in a position to fill the gap this created.

Of the total Rumanian production, the Soviet Union takes about 20 per cent as reparations. Of the remaining 80 per cent, half is required by Rumania proper and the other half is at the disposal of the Soviet Union for export. So it is that in 1950, of the total production, about 2.6 million tons went to Russia, while only 1.7 million tons remained in Rumania. The great interest of the Soviet Union in Rumanian oil deliveries is shown by the fact that in 1950 a pipeline was constructed from the Rumanian oil center, Ploesti, to the Russian Black Sea port of Odessa, making possible direct shipment of Rumanian oil to Russia. Since the end of the war a slow rise in Rumanian oil production can be observed, but it is very doubtful that the prewar production of 8.7 million tons will be reached again. Under these conditions, it is improbable that Rumanian oil exports will exceed 4 million tons in the near future.

Hungary and Albania: Oil imports from Hungary and Albania, both of which belong to the Eastern Bloc, are insignificant for the Soviet Union because production in Hungary was only 550,000 tons and in Albania only 350,000 tons.[36]

Czechoslovakia and Eastern Germany: Czechoslovakia and Eastern Germany have no oil deposits but have built large synthetic-motor-fuel industries. In Eastern Germany synthetic-oil production was about 800,000 tons in 1949 and may have surpassed 1,000,000 tons in

---

than 3,000,000 tons, the Rumanian Five-Year Plan for 1951 to 1955, which was decreed on December 14, 1950, places oil production in 1949 at 4,814,000 tons and in 1950 at 5,464,000 tons. See *Erdöl und Kohle*, IV (1951), 220.

[35] Translator's note: Figures for 1951 and 1952 added by translator from private sources.

[36] Translator's note: Reliable sources estimate Hungary's 1952 production at 500,000 tons and Albania's at 200,000 tons. But see "Report from Hungary," in the *Oil and Gas Journal*, June 8, 1953, p. 79. See, further, *World Oil*, July 1953, p. 252, where discovery of a major oil field in Northeast Hungary is mentioned.

1950. Czechoslovakia has the capacity to produce about 1,500,000 tons of synthetic motor fuel annually. Imports of synthetic motor fuel into the Soviet Union from these two areas can be estimated at about 1 million tons.

Austria: Soviet imports of oil from Austria are a problem insofar as they involve several uncertain factors. The Austrian oil deposits, centering chiefly around Ziestersdorf and Matzen, lie entirely in the Soviet zone of occupation. However, Austria does not belong to the Eastern Bloc. All Austrian oil-concession areas were seized by the Soviets as German property and are operated by them. Important new discoveries have succeeded in increasing Austrian oil production. At present it is estimated at 1.5 to 1.8 million tons.[37] Of this total production Austria keeps comparatively little. The remainder is exported. Until 1949 about 50 per cent of the Austrian production was shipped to Western Europe, where it was sold for dollars. These exports to the West are now completely prohibited by the Russians and diverted to the Soviet Union.

Imports from all these countries may have been about five million tons in 1950 and should not exceed six to eight million tons in the years to come, even if the intensive exploration of these countries should be successful. At the present, Russia's oil imports are about one eighth of its oil production.

Sinkiang: All imports dealt with so far originate in European countries and go to the European portion of the Soviet Union. The only prospective oil area in Asia from which the Soviet Union may eventually get oil, on account of direct participation, is Sinkiang, the East Chinese province. The economic development of this province was agreed upon by Moscow and Peking in the Russo-Chinese treaty of March 27, 1950. Exploration is carried on by a Russo-Chinese oil company in which the Soviet Union owns a 50-per-cent share. Naturally, oil production in Sinkiang would be important to the Central Asiatic industrial area of the Soviet Union. However, it cannot be assumed that this exploration will lead to oil exports to Soviet Russia in the near future.[38]

[37] According to *Erdöl-Informationdienst* of February 1, 1951, Austrian oil production was only 900,000 tons in 1950. This figure is certainly too low. See Table 38 in the Author's Appendix to this book.

[38] See Anton Zischka, *op.cit.*, p. 175, where he says: "The Russians are particularly interested in the oil fields of Wusu (where small quantities of high-quality oil have been produced since 1909). Ten different oil districts are known in Sinkiang. Enormous areas on both sides of the Tien Shan Mountains are considered highly promising by

However, at best, all these possibilities of imports can mean only a supplementary oil supply for the Soviet Union. The core of the Soviet oil industry will always be the Russian oil fields. These imports are not sufficient to increase Russia's strength economically and politically. To reach this goal steps must be taken transcending economics and leading directly into the "Alpine regions of world politics." Therefore, at the end of this survey it is necessary to point out the tensions and dangers which exist in Soviet relations with the Middle East.

---

the Americans. Oil is particularly important for Sinkiang because its ancient 'silk road' assumed new significance in World War II. It has since become the carrier of the largest amount of motor-truck traffic in China."

EPILOGUE

THE SOVIET UNION AND THE
MIDDLE EAST

THE SOVIET UNION AND THE
MIDDLE EAST

THE center of world politics today is the most promising oil region of the globe, the Middle East, where the oil wealth of Iran, Iraq, Saudi Arabia, Kuwait, Qatar, and Bahrein Island amounts to more than 40 per cent of the total world oil reserves.[1] Three "continents"—America, Europe, and the Soviet Union—are immediately interested in this region.

American, British, and Dutch oil concerns own these concessions. They have invested huge sums in Middle Eastern oil industries for exploration and development. For instance, the investment of the Anglo-Iranian Oil Company in Iran is about one billion dollars. These oil companies are backed up by the political, military, and economic strength of the United States and Great Britain, which will never voluntarily give up these pillars of their power.

Europe, as well as America, is closely connected with the fate of the Middle East. By far the largest part of Europe's great demand for oil is filled from Middle Eastern production. A change or even a shift in the balance of power in the Middle East might easily become for Europe a question of survival.[2]

This rich oil area lies on Russia's immediate doorstep. All the problems of the Soviet oil industry—the supply difficulties and the oil bottlenecks—would be solved at one stroke and eliminated forever if the Soviet Union succeeded in getting a foothold in the Middle East or became a dominating power. In this light, present events in Iran assume special significance. The Soviet Union has long tried to obtain oil concessions in Iran, but negotiations have never terminated in a contractual agreement.

A unanimous resolution of the Iranian Parliament on March 15, 1951 demanded nationalization of the country's entire oil industry. This has suddenly and surprisingly opened up new vistas the economic and political consequences of which cannot be ascertained at

[1] Translator's note: Middle East reserves are 55 per cent of the world total, and, if the United States is excluded, about 72 per cent. *Oil and Gas Journal*, December 22, 1952, p. 180.

[2] "In the Middle East meet not only all the roads and supply lines from the West; there are the most prolific oil wells on earth; . . . for Europe this oil is cheaper than the oil from America. Transportation routes are shorter. It is expected that Europe from 1952 on will cover almost its entire oil demand in the Middle East." *Le Monde*, Paris, January 27, 1951.

present. This resolution has understandably shocked not only Great Britain, which is primarily concerned, but the rest of the Western World as well. (The Anglo-Iranian Oil Company owns all important oil concessions in Iran and in 1950 alone produced practically all of an Iranian total of 32 million tons.) Months before that resolution, Andrew Roth wrote in the *London Tribune* of September 15, 1950, as follows: "Persia is far more important for the Soviets than Korea. Convincing proof of how important Persia is for the Kremlin is given by a seized copy of the minutes of the meeting of Hitler and Molotov in November 1940. Asked about Soviet demands, Molotov requested control over the Dardanelles and the right of the Soviet Union to expand south of Batumi and Baku in the general direction of the Persian Gulf."

Walter Bedell Smith, former American ambassador to Moscow, reports in his book, *My Three Years in Moscow*, a talk with Stalin which deserves special attention: "Stalin spoke then in detail on the Persian oil question, including a history of Soviet-Iranian relations since the Treaty of Versailles. He emphasized how important it was for the Soviet Union to get a larger share in the exploitation of the world oil deposits and maintained that first Britain and then the United States had laid obstacles in her way when she endeavored to obtain oil concessions. 'You don't understand our position as regards oil in Persia,' said Stalin literally. 'The oil fields of Baku are our main source of raw material in this regard. They lie in the immediate vicinity of the Persian border and are very vulnerable. Beria (the head of the MVD) and others tell me that saboteurs—and be it only one man with a box of matches—could cause serious damage at any time. We are not going to permit our oil supply to be endangered.' "[3]

Without doubt the Russians aim at securing oil delivery from the Middle East to the Soviet Union and preventing the establishment of military bases in the Middle East by Western powers. It is to the interest of the Soviet Union in the long run to "eliminate the Middle East from the Anglo-American sphere of interest."

Since the Soviet Union, under a Russo-Iranian agreement, can send troops to Iran for protection, "as soon as a third power threatens Iranian independence,"[4] serious consequences may ensue from these

[3] Walter Bedell Smith, *Meine drei Jahre in Moskau* (Hamburg, 1950), p. 66. (Translator's note: Mr. Smith is the present Undersecretary of State.)

[4] See "Verstaatlichung der persischen Erdölindustrie" in *Erdöl und Kohle*, IV (1951), 162.

conflicting interests. Thus the Middle East has become a nerve center in world politics. If some day the production of the Middle East, which will exceed 100 million tons in the years to come, should be added to Russian oil production, presently at 40 million tons, this would mean such an increase in economic power for the Soviet Union that the political aspect of the world would be altered, too.[5]

[5] Translator's note: "Russia is an enormous country with rapidly expanding industries, and her chief oilfield, at Baku, is growing old. Now, if a giant, standing on the frosty Caucasus, were to look towards the warm-water ports of the Persian Gulf, it would be clear to him that if he advanced in that direction (cutting as he did so the air communications that link Britain and the rest of Europe with India, Australia and the Far East) he could tread on an oilfield at every step: North Iran, Iraq, South Iran, Kuwait, Saudi Arabia, Bahrain, Qatar. It is important to keep in mind the difference between the holding of a concession and permanent command over the resources which it represents. In peace-time the companies which hold the concessions for Middle East oil market it on commercial principles—and Russia, of course, can buy from them as much as she wishes; but who would command those resources in the unhappy event of another war? The nearness of Russia, with her immense reserves of man-power, militarized from childhood, is a factor which must be taken into account." Quoted from Sir Reader Bullard, *Britain and the Middle East, from the Earliest Times to 1950* (London, 1951), pp. 165-166.

AUTHOR'S APPENDIX

AUTHOR'S APPENDIX

Table 37. Russian Crude-Oil Production, 1861-1950, Compared with World and American Crude-Oil Production
(thousands of tons)

Year	World	U.S.A.	USSR
1861	293	286	3
1862	425	413	4
1863	380	353	6
1864	317	286	9
1865	374	338	9
1866	537	486	11
1867	530	452	17
1868	549	493	12
1869	646	570	28
1870	798	711	28
1871	789	703	23
1872	946	850	25
1873	1,492	1,337	65
1874	1,642	1,476	80
1875	1,373	1,187	96
1876	1,521	1,234	182
1877	2,168	1,804	248
1878	2,535	2,080	330
1879	3,248	2,691	380
1880	4,131	3,552	413
1881	4,403	3,737	496
1882	4,914	4,101	625
1883	4,164	3,168	826
1884	4,950	3,272	1,487
1885	5,060	2,954	1,916
1886	6,502	3,792	2,478
1887	6,580	3,822	2,528
1888	7,179	3,731	3,172
1889	8,465	4,751	3,387
1890	10,547	6,192	3,949
1891	12,538	7,336	4,758
1892	12,213	6,824	4,924
1893	12,669	6,544	5,568
1894	12,295	6,667	5,006
1895	14,271	7,147	6,350
1896	15,717	8,237	6,499
1897	16,790	8,171	7,487
1898	17,201	7,481	8,479

TABLE 37 (*continued*)

Year	World	U.S.A.	USSR
1899	18,049	7,711	9,077
1900	20,525	8,596	10,429
1901	23,044	9,376	11,721
1902	25,022	11,994	11,085
1903	26,821	13,574	10,403
1904	29,996	15,820	10,809
1905	29,602	18,203	7,564
1906	29,351	17,091	8,106
1907	36,328	22,442	8,512
1908	39,263	24,122	8,559
1909	41,111	24,749	9,079
1910	45,109	28,315	9,680
1911	47,393	29,786	9,108
1912	48,506	30,122	9,361
1913	53,034	33,569	8,648
1914	56,089	35,909	9,222
1915	59,460	37,982	9,434
1916	62,964	40,637	9,058
1917	69,212	45,307	8,680
1918	69,297	48,092	3,739
1919	76,504	51,124	4,370
1920	94,809	59,847	3,500
1921	105,523	63,800	3,987
1922	118,208	75,332	4,913
1923	139,793	98,961	5,388
1924	139,598	96,465	6,255
1925	147,114	103,195	7,231
1926	150,953	104,158	8,878
1927	173,766	121,758	10,665
1928	182,325	121,804	11,763
1929	204,496	136,106	13,862
1930	194,060	121,336	17,545
1931	188,898	114,995	22,814
1932	180,247	106,088	21,632
1933	198,479	122,369	21,654
1934	209,507	122,695	24,487
1935	227,703	134,657	25,475
1936	246,565	148,586	26,099
1937	280,654	172,836	27,103
1938	273,609	164,080	28,770
1939	287,113	170,918	30,435
1940	295,174	182,842	30,673

TABLE 37 (*concluded*)

Year	World	U.S.A.	USSR
1941	305,623	189,465	33,364
1942	288,068	187,359	31,894
1943	310,573	203,434	28,364
1944	356,800	226,713	38,583
1945	357,131	231,544	21,382
1946	378,018	234,284	22,582
1947	415,914	250,791	26,830
1948	470,431	277,000	30,500
1949	469,275	252,996	33,200
1950	522,840	270,000	37,600
1861-1950 included	9,021,099	5,540,164	915,976

Sources: Figures for 1861 through 1946 from *World Oil*, International Operations Issue, July 15, 1949; figures for 1947 through 1950 from other sources.

Statistics on Russian oil production vary considerably, especially for 1940 through 1950. Shimkin ("Is Petroleum a Soviet Weakness?" The *Oil and Gas Journal*, December 21, 1950) estimates Russian production in 1942 at 18 million tons. His figures for 1945 (19.5 million tons), 1946 (21.7 million tons), 1947 (27.9 million tons), and 1948 (29.2 million tons) are closer to those given by the author. *World Oil*'s figure for 1944 (275 million barrels) seems too high.

TABLE 38. World Crude-Oil Production, 1948-1950
(thousands of tons)

Country	1948	1949	1950
U.S.A.	277,000	252,996	270,000
Venezuela	69,000	69,012	78,000
USSR	30,500	33,200	37,600
Iran	25,300	27,235	31,800
Saudi Arabia	19,260	23,471	27,000
Kuwait	6,400	12,378	17,200
Mexico	8,500	8,724	10,600
Indonesia	3,980	5,930	7,200
Iraq	3,153	4,200	6,200
Colombia	3,250	4,163	4,800
British Borneo	2,770	3,540	4,500
Rumania	4,300	4,300	4,300[a]
Canada	1,447	2,829	3,600
Argentina	3,300	3,151	3,500
Trinidad	2,900	3,050	3,100
Egypt	1,830	2,280	2,300
Peru	1,850	1,979	1,900
Qatar	....	100	1,600
Bahrein	1,500	1,508	1,500

TABLE 38 (concluded)

Country	1948	1949	1950
Germany	635	840	1,100
Austria	1,080	900	900[b]
Netherlands	500	621	700
Hungary	480	510	550
Yugoslavia	55	340	400
Albania	60	325	350
Ecuador	360	337	350
Others	1,021	1,356	1,790
Total	470,431	469,275	522,840

[a] Other sources show 5.5 million tons.
[b] Other sources show 1.5 to 1.8 million tons.
Sources: Figures for 1948 are from *Erdöl-Informationsdienst*, January 15, 1950; those for 1949 and 1950 are from the February 1, 1951 issue of the same publication.

TABLE 39. Terms for Various Oil Products

Germany	England	United States	Soviet Union
Erdgas	Natural gas	Natural gas	Gaz
Erdöl	Petroleum	Crude oil	Neft
Rohöl	Crude oil	Petroleum	Neft
Benzin	Motor spirit; petrol	Gasoline; naphtha	Benzin
Petroleum	Kerosine	Kerosene	Kerosin
Leuchtöl	Paraffin	Kerosene	Kerosin
Gasöl	Gas oil	Gas oil	Solyarovoye
Solaröl	Solar oil[a]	Solar oil[a]	Maslo
Schmieröl	Lubricants (various kinds)	Lubricants (various kinds)	Smazocnoye maslo
Heizöl	Fuel oil residue	Fuel oil residue	Mayut ostatki
Paraffin	Paraffin wax	Paraffin wax	Parafin
Asphalt	Asphalt	Asphalt	Asphalt
Vaseline	Petroleum jelly	Vaseline	Vaselina

[a] Translator's note: Solar oil means any of various mineral oils used as fuel or illuminating oils, especially a gas oil made from petroleum or an intermediate fraction made from crude shale oil. *Webster's New International Dictionary* (2nd ed., unabridged; Springfield, Mass., 1937).
Source: *Erdöl und Kohle*, III (1950), 96.

TABLE 40. Classification of Reserves of Mineral Deposits According to the Decree of the Council of the People's Commissars of the Soviet Union, February 14, 1951

Status of Exploration and Recovery of Mineral Reserves	Industrial Importance of the Reserves
Class A-1	
Absolutely proved and sampled reserves. The size of the deposits is based on an appraisal by mining techniques. The exploration of the properties and technology for refining have been established on a commercial scale.	Basis of plans for development.
Class A-2	
Thoroughly explored and sampled reserves which have been confirmed by mining or drilling, or both. The testing of the properties and the technology for refining the useful mineral have been established with typical specimens.	Basis of technical projects and financial investments; also, in certain cases, for indefinite plan of recovery.
Class B	
Reserves which have been proved by prospecting with sufficient exactness. The form of the mineral body, the distribution of the mineral species, and the technology for refining have not been clarified sufficiently.	Basis of technical projects and capital investment if reserves of Class A also exist. In complicated deposits, the reserves for technical projects and investments are to be separated.
Class C-1	
Probable reserves contiguous to developed reserves of the higher classes (A and B). Also, reserves which are suspected to exist because of geological prospecting according to natural and theoretical indications or geophysical data. Largely undeveloped reserves with particularly complex distribution or without orderly distribution in the composite, or reserves which have been tested only in isolated spots.	Basis for the drafting of an industrial plan and of the financial needs for geological exploration. Investment of capital is also possible for complicated deposits of valuable minerals though certain reserves have been proved to belong in higher classes.

TABLE 40 (*concluded*)

Status of Exploration and Recovery of Mineral Reserves	Industrial Importance of the Reserves
Class C-2	
Potential reserves of incidental occurrence, the existence of which is based on geological opinion. Also, possible reserves in a group of deposits, mineralized zones, or entire areas for which geological opinion is the authority.	

Source: T. Klie, *Russisch-Deutsche Wörterbuch* (Königsberg, 1945).

TRANSLATOR'S APPENDIX, BIBLIOGRAPHY, AND INDEX

TRANSLATOR'S APPENDIX

Conversion Factors

The author gives all oil-production figures in metric tons. He says: "In American statistics production figures are quoted in barrels. On an average, seven barrels are equal to one ton. The exact conversion of barrels into tons depends, however, upon the specific gravity of the oils. The United States Bureau of Mines figures in the case of U.S. oil, that 7.401 barrels are equal to one ton, and, in the case of Russian oil, that 7.266 barrels are equal to one ton. This leads to certain discrepancies in comparing statistics based on higher or lower coefficients."

Other Conversion Factors

1 meter = 1.094 yards = 3.281 feet = 39.37 inches = 0.001 kilometers
1 kilometer = 1,000 meters = 0.621 miles
1 cubic meter = 35.3148 cubic feet
1 metric ton = 0.98421 long ton = 1.1023 short tons = 2,204.6 pounds
1 kilowatt-hour = 3,411 British thermal units

TABLE 41. World Oil Production[a]
1950-1951
(millions of barrels)[b]

	1950	1951	1952
U.S.A.	2,155.5	2,245.0	2,294.0
Venezuela	547.1	623.4	660.0
USSR and Eastern Europe	308.5	341.4	342.0
Saudi Arabia	199.5	278.0	300.1
Kuwait	125.7	204.9	274.1
Iran	241.4	125.0	10.7
Mexico	74.6	79.6	78.8
Iraq	49.8	64.6	139.0
Indonesia	47.9	56.1	61.7
Canada	29.1	48.1	61.6
Colombia	34.8	39.1	39.3
British Borneo	31.0	37.5	38.5
Argentina	23.5	25.1	24.3
Trinidad	20.9	21.0	21.0
Qatar	12.3	18.3	25.0
Peru	16.1	17.2	16.9
Egypt	16.4	16.4	16.4
Austria	11.3	14.7	21.0
Bahrein	11.0	11.0	11.0
Western Germany	8.0	9.7	12.2
Netherlands	4.9	5.0	5.0
Ecuador	2.8	2.9	2.8

TABLE 41 (*concluded*)

	1950	1951	1952
France	1.1	2.4	2.5
Japan	2.1	2.3	2.1
India	2.0	2.0	2.0
New Guinea	1.8	1.8	1.8
Others	5.6	8.2	8.2
Total	3,984.6	4,300.7	4,547.0

a Translator's note: This table brings up to date the figures given by the author in Table 38.

b Seven to seven and one-half barrels equal one metric ton. One barrel contains 42 U.S. gallons.

Sources: Private.

TABLE 42. Basic Production
(millions of metric tons)

	U.S.A. 1951	United Kingdom, France, and West Germany combined 1951	USSR 1951	planned for 1955
Coal	523.0	398.4	281.0	372.0
Oil	309.0	1.7	42.3	70.0
Electricity[a]	370.2	147.4	103.0	162.5
Pig iron	63.9	29.3	22.1	34.1
Crude steel	95.4	39.2	31.3	44.2

a Millions of kilowatt-hours.

Source: The *Economist* (London), August 30, 1952.

TABLE 43. Per-Capita Production
(kilograms)

	U.S.A. 1951	United Kingdom 1951	Germany 1951	France 1951	USSR 1951	planned for 1955
Coal	3,500	4,500	2,480	1,250	1,384	1,730
Oil	2,050	1	29	7	208	325
Electricity[a]	2,468	1,199	1,070	850	500	756
Pig iron	426	197	233	286	109	159
Steel	635	317	281	232	154	206

a Kilowatt-hours.

Source: *ibid.*

ABOUT THE DEVELOPMENT OF THE SECOND BAKU

An excellent description of the development of the Second Baku region which resembles closely the oil-boom stories of times past in this country is found in *Erdöl und Kohle*,[1] a German oil journal. Of utmost importance, the well-written report reads as follows:

"The twentieth anniversary of the discovery of oil in the Bashkir Autonomous SSR which meant the beginning of the Second Baku was the topic of many articles in the Soviet press. . . . Tribute was paid to the accomplishments of I. M. Gubkin, Soviet oil geologist, and his pupil A. A. Blochin. Following Gubkin's directions Blochin did exploratory drilling on the right and left banks of the Belaya River near the village of Ishimbayevo. On May 16, 1932 one of these drillings resulted in a tremendous gusher. Two weeks later, oil gushers were drilled on the other bank of the river. These successes caused Stalin to decree, in the Seventeenth Congress of the Communist Party, 'promotion of the oil industry on the western and southern slopes of the Urals by all means.' Since then this part of the Bashkir Republic has been completely transformed. New railroads and asphalt-covered auto highways have been built. Pipelines and high-tension lines are traversing this area. Three big oil cities have come into being: Ishimbay, Oktyabr'skiy, and Chernikovsk. In the Second Baku the Bashkir Autonomous SSR with its oil production occupies a leading position with regard both to quantity and to production techniques. The most modern methods of exploratory drilling and exploitation have been developed. Rotary drilling in Bashkir has been completely replaced by turbine drilling and electro-drilling. This has made possible an increase of drilling footage to 3,900 feet per month despite the hard rocks. The oil in the Ufa region is mainly Devonian. Pipelines connect the oil deposits of Ishimbay and its vicinity and those of Tuymazy with Ufa, capital of the Bashkir Autonomous SSR. The oil of the Second Baku is being refined in several newly built refineries; among them is a refinery at Ufa with an average annual throughput capacity in 1950 of about 1,500,000 tons, another one at Ishimbay with about 450,000 tons, a third refinery at Sterlitamak with about 750,000 tons, and finally one at Tuymazy with about 500,000 tons. A petroleum institute[2] and a geological research institute have been established in Ufa, and two more petroleum institutes in Ishimbay and Tuymazy. Oil production in Bashkir in 1952 is reported to exceed last year's [i.e., 1951] production by 23.7%. At the same time a substantial increase in the throughput capacity of the refineries has been scheduled for 1952."

According to Dr. Smirnov, former leading Arctic geologist, now a consultant for Socony-Vacuum, "the Second Baku basin . . . has been developed from the Caspian Sea for more than 800 miles northward." "But it actually extends all the way from the Caspian Sea to the Arctic and north to Franz Josef Land."[3]

[1] v (1952), 525.
[2] Translator's note: These institutes are schools for training petroleum technicians.
[3] L. P. Smirnov, "Soviet Oil: The Inside Story," *The Flying Red Horse*, summer 1953, pp. 2-4.

LATEST DEVELOPMENTS
An Improvement in the Russian Oil Situation

On the occasion of the Nineteenth Congress of the Communist Party of the Soviet Union held in October 1952 in Moscow, some important facts were revealed which show a definite improvement in the Russian oil situation and bear out the guarded predictions of the author of this book.

For the first time, the figures and targets for the fifth Five-Year Plan of the Soviet Union, covering the period 1951-1955, were announced; another authentic source was a departmental report to the Party Congress by Mr. Baibakov, Minister for the Oil Industry. Other information, too, gives some interesting clues.

The target for crude-oil production in 1955 is 70 million tons (about 509 million barrels) but Mr. Baibakov believes that production will be somewhat higher than 70 million tons by then. Production in 1952 is estimated at 47 million tons (about 342 million barrels). According to Mr. Baibakov more than 50 per cent of this year's production will have come from the eastern districts, 40 per cent from the Second Baku alone.

Beside the Second Baku, the eastern districts include the Emba region, Ukhta-Pechora, Sakhalin, and the fields in Central Asia. The oil-bearing area in the Tatar Autonomous Soviet Socialist Republic in the Middle Volga region, which was discovered under the fourth Five-Year Plan, has now been developed into an important producing area.[1]

Mr. Baibakov attributed the increased production to a much higher rate of drilling. He stated that over 40 per cent of all drilling at present is "turbo-drilling"[2] a method claimed by the Russians to be highly successful. Employment of (American) secondary-recovery techniques is another factor in the more favorable picture. Offshore drilling in the Caspian Sea is also being carried out and has met with a certain amount of success; in these operations directional drilling is being used. Mr. Baibakov, finally, reported that exploration work undertaken on a wide scale in the past nine years has greatly increased Russia's (known) oil and gas reserves, which the Soviet technical press reported as being as high as 4.5 billion tons now, against 1 billion tons in 1938.

The Russians claim discoveries of new oil regions of undisclosed location. In this connection a dispatch in *Erdöl und Kohle*[3] which is taken from *Erdöldienst*, Vienna, deserves mentioning. It tells about opening up important oil fields along the northern coast of Siberia. The structures are said to be salt domes. The famous Soviet geologist Gubkin, whose work led to the discovery of the Second Baku, early pointed to Siberia as an oil-rich region. The starting point was Arkhangelsk. A base for operations

[1] This information with much which precedes and follows it, unless indicated otherwise, is quoted from articles on Russian oil in the October and November 1952 issues of *Petroleum Press Service* of London.

[2] See supra, p. 44.

[3] v (1952), 607. See also Smirnov, *op.cit.*; and *Erdöl und Kohle*, vi (1953), 360, where new oil production in the Lena River basin, with Yakutsk as the center, is reported.

was established at Nordvik where coal mines supplied the energy for drilling. The discovery well had a depth of only 2,000 feet. Production of the fields at Nordvik and Ust (Ust-Port?) is reported to be 160,000 tons annually at the present time.

Not only crude-oil production, but also shale-oil production is to be increased.[4] Further, production of natural gas, in which Russia is very rich, is to be stepped up. A one-million-ton-capacity hydrogenation plant at Lake Baykal, producing oil from coal, is scheduled for completion and operation in 1953. This "achievement" is due to dismantling of the former German hydrogenation plants at Poelitz and Blechhammer and rebuilding them on Russian soil!

Especially important is the target of the fifth Five-Year Plan for refinery capacity. It is to be doubled within the five-year period. New refineries will be built near the consuming centers rather than near the oil fields.[5] Percentage yields of "light products"—gasoline, kerosene, and gas oil—are to be raised in order to meet the anticipated great increase in military needs. This is especially true for jet-aircraft fuel—jet aircrafts are high in favor with the Russians.

Also, transportation, a weak point of the Russian oil industry, is to be improved through construction of oil pipelines.[6] Another very vulnerable spot, the manufacture of oil equipment, is to be increased to 3.5 times its size.

Erdöl und Kohle[7] reported recently a series of complaints in the official party organ *Pravda* (Moscow) about the poor quality of drill bits used in the Groznyy oil district. Another serious obstacle to Russian oil production is the abundance of paraffin contained in the crude oil of Tuymazy (Ufa Region), next to Syzran the richest area of the Second Baku.[8]

Nothing is known about demand or consumption.[9] Certainly, the increasing requirements of transportation, agriculture, and other sectors of the economy put a strain on the supply-demand balance, which may continue to be tight. Exports to China and North Korea are probably compensated for by larger production from Austrian fields and those of satellite countries. But competent observers believe that the targets set in the fifth Five-Year Plan will be reached.[10]

---

[4] For instance, oil-shale deposits are being opened up at the village of Kashpir, near Syzran in the Kuybyshev area. *Erdöl und Kohle*, VI (1953), 109.

[5] See *Petroleum Press Service*, October 1952, p. 349.

[6] There are, according to Dr. Smirnov, *op.cit.*, at least 20 refineries and more than 1,000 miles of pipeline in the Second Baku region. One pipeline goes across the Ural Mountains into Siberia.

[7] V (1952), 681-682. [8] *ibid.*, pp. 681-682.

[9] D. B. Shimkin in his book *Minerals—A Key to Soviet Power* (Cambridge, Mass., 1953) estimates the Soviet's 1950 consumption of petroleum at 35,000 metric tons, and of natural gas at 91,780,000,000 cubic feet.

[10] An Associated Press dispatch from Moscow in the *New York Times* on January 1, 1953 says that according to the Soviet press, 1952 plans for production of oil in the Soviet Union were over-fulfilled. The rise in output continued in the Second Baku region, in the Bashkir and Tatar areas, and in the Urals. Development in these places in 1952 was supposed to have been particularly intense.

In the foreign field, recent policy moves of the Russians clearly prove the desire to gain access to the oil-rich regions of the Middle East by wooing the peoples of that turbulent area. This and the serious production efforts should keep us on guard. The danger is real.

TRANSLATOR'S BIBLIOGRAPHY

Balzak, Vasyutin, and Feigin (eds.). *Economic Geography of the USSR.* Trans. Robert M. Hankin and Olga A. Titelbaum. American edition ed. by Chauncy D. Harris. New York: Macmillan, 1949.

Baykov, Alexander. *The Development of the Soviet Economic System.* Cambridge: Cambridge University Press, 1946.

Bullard, Sir Reader. *Britain and the Middle East, from the Earliest Times to 1950.* London: Hutchinson's University Library, 1951.

Caroe, Sir Olaf. *Wells of Power: The Oil Fields of Southwestern Asia, a Regional and Global Study.* London: Macmillan, 1951.

Duff, Dahl M. "Refining in Russia," *The Oil and Gas Journal*, Refinery Number, March 17, 1952, p. 181.

Fohs, F. Julius. "Petroliferous Provinces of U.S.S.R.," *Bulletin, American Association of Petroleum Geologists*, Vol. 32, No. 3 (March 1948), pp. 317-350, bibliography.

Jurin, M. N. "Can Russia Produce 600 M. Bbls. of Oil Annually by 1955?" *World Oil*, March 1953, pp. 236ff.

Leeston, Alfred M. *Magic Oil, Servant of the World.* Dallas: Juan Pablos Books, 1951.

Lenczowski, George. *The Middle East in World Affairs.* Ithaca: Cornell Cornell University Press, 1949.

Lenczowski, George. *The Middle East in World Affairs.* Ithaca: Cornell University Press, 1952.

Malzahn, E. "Geologie und Erdölführung der russischen Tafel und des Embagebietes." I: "Structuren, Fazies und Erdölführung im Mittleren Wolgagebiet (im 'Zweiten Baku')," *Erdöl und Kohle*, v (1952), 371ff. II: "Ölgeologische und Stratigraphische Probleme im europäischen Teil der U d S S R," *ibid.*, pp. 438ff. (These articles are derived from scientific Russian sources and are of basic importance.)

Norins, Martin R. *Gateway to Asia: Sinkiang.* New York: John Day, 1944.

"Oil in the USSR," *Focus*, Vol. 1, No. 2 (November 15, 1950). New York: American Geographical Society.

Pratt, Wallace E. and Good, Dorothy (eds.). *World Geography of Petroleum.* American Geographical Society Special Publication No. 31. Princeton: Princeton University Press, 1950. Especially Stebinger, Eugene. "The Union of Soviet Socialist Republics," pp. 230-239; bibliography, pp. 423ff.

Rosu, George G. "Iron-Curtain Report: Four Articles on the Petroleum Industry in the Eastern European Countries Controlled by Russia," the *Oil and Gas Journal*, June 2, 1952, pp. 63ff.; June 9, 1952, pp. 57ff.; June 16, 1952, pp. 182ff.; and June 30, 1952, pp. 47ff.

Schwartz, Harry. *Russia's Soviet Economy.* New York: Prentice-Hall, 1951.

Shabad, Theodore. *Geography of the USSR.* New York: Columbia University Press, 1951. (Up-to-date, excellent.)

Shimkin, Demitri B. "Is Petroleum a Soviet Weakness?" The *Oil and Gas Journal*, December 21, 1950, pp. 214ff.

Shimkin, Demitri B. *Minerals—A Key to Soviet Power*. Cambridge: Harvard University Press, 1953.

Smirnov, Leonid. "Oil in Russia," *World Oil*, October and December 1951; May and June 1952. (Geological study by a former leading Russian geologist.)

Smirnov, Leonid. "Soviet Oil: The Inside Story," *The Flying Red Horse*, summer 1953, pp. 2-4.

Thompson, O. Beeby. *The Oil Fields of Russia and the Russian Petroleum Industry*. London: Crosby Lockwood and Son, 1908.

Velikovsky, A. S. (ed.). *Handbook on the Oil Deposits of the Soviet Union*. Solid Fuel and Geol.–Res. Lit., 1938 and 1948. (In Russian.)

Wartanoff, Boris. *Le Pétrole Russe*. Paris: La Presse Française et Étrangère, 1945. (Interesting, brief account.)

Wszelaki, Jan. "Petroleum for Power in Red Europe," *World Oil*, May 1952, pp. 252ff.

For other publications in Russian, see: Siegrist, Marie, *et al. Bibliography and Index of Geology of North America*. New York: Geological Society of America, 1940 to 1950.

INDEX

INDEX

Abuzy oil field (Maykop area), 74
Academy of Science (Moscow), 39, 42n; geological-geographical department of, 39
Achi-Su oil field (Dagestan area), 71 (*map*), 75
Afghanistan, 3, 101 (*map*), 102
agriculture, motorization of, 58f.; oil consumption of, 58f., 59n.; tractors in, 58f.
agrotowns, 118
airways, 57f.
Ak-Mecket oil field (Fergana area), 102
Aktyubinsk, 94, 96 (*map*)
Aktyubneft trust, 35, 95
Albania, 135
Ali Yurt oil field (Groznyy area), 70
Alkasovo oil field (Groznyy area), 70
Allaguvatovo oil field (Second Baku), 91
Alma-Ata, 9
Amderma, 98 (*map*), 99
Amu Darya River, 100 (*map*)
Amur River, 104 (*map*), 105
Andizhan, 52, 100 (*map*), 102
Andizhan oil and gas field (Fergana area), 100 (*map*), 102
Anglo-Iranian Oil Company, 141
anticlines, *see* oil geology
Apsheronneft trust, 34
Apsheronsk oil field (Maykop area), 71 (*map*), 74
Apsheron Peninsula, 23, 24
Arctic Ocean, 5, 5 (*map*), 98 (*map*), 99
Armavir, 71 (*map*), 72, 74
Arkhangelsk, 48 (*map*), 98 (*map*), 158
Armenian SSR, 9
Armenians, 6
Artem Island oil field (Baku area), 68
Artemneft trust, 34, 67
Asphalt Mountain oil field (Maykop area), 74
Ashkhabad, 9, 76 (*map*), 77
Associated Press, 95n., 159n.
Astrakhan, 31, 69, 71 (*map*)
Austria, 136
automobiles, production of, 57
aviation gasoline, 59, 95n., *see also* products
Azerbaijan SSR, 9, 67
Azerbaijani, ethnic group, 6
Azizbekovneft trust, 34, 67
Azneft group, 34, 67

Baibakov, Minister for the Oil Industry, 34, 54n., 158

Bakovichi oil field (Groznyy area), 70
Baku, city, 30, 52, 37 (*map*), 67, 68 (*map*); pipelines from, 68; refineries in, 68
Baku oil region, 9, 23f., 24, 25, 26, 37 (*map*), 43, 52, 67ff., 68 (*map*); production in, 68f.; transportation in, 69f.; vulnerability in war of, 70; *and passim*
Baladzhary oil field (Baku area), 68, 68 (*map*)
Balakhany oil field (Baku area), 23, 26, 67, 68 (*map*)
Baltic Sea, 3
Balzak, 161
Barents Sea, 98 (*map*), 99
Barzik oil field (Fergana area), 102
Bashkir Autonomous SSR, 88 (*map*), 157
Bashneft group, 34, 89
basic production of U.S.A. and USSR in 1951, 156 (*table*)
Batraki, 91, 92 (*map*)
Batumi (or Batum), 30, 31, 52, 68 (*map*); pipeline to Baku, 68, 69, 75
Baychunas oil field (Emba area), 95, 96 (*map*), 97
Baykov, Alexander, 14n., 161
Belaya River, 89, 90 (*map*), 157
Belorussian SSR, 9
Berekei oil field (Dagestan area), 75
Berg, L. S., 5n.
Bergins, Friedrich, 132
Beria, L. P., 142
Beriyaneft trust, 34, 67
Bibi-Eybat oil field (Baku area), 23, 67, 68, 68 (*map*); 1882 "gusher" in, 24; underwater drilling near, 43
Binagady oil field (Baku area), 23, 67, 68 (*map*)
Bistrie oil field (Western Ukraine), 81
Black Sea, 25, 31, 75, *and passim*
Blechhammer, 159
Blochin, A. A., 157
Bolshevik, 118n.
Borislav, 78 (*map*), 81
Borislav oil and gas field (Western Ukraine), 78 (*map*), 81
Brantly, J. E., 118n.
Bug River, 3, 78 (*map*)
Buguruslanneft trust, 35, 91
Buguruslan oil and gas field (Second Baku), 52, 90 (*map*), 91, 92 (*map*)
Bulganin, Marshal, 58
Bullard, Sir Reader, 143n., 161
Buranchino oil field (Second Baku), 89, 90 (*map*)

Buzovnyneft trust, 34, 67
Bytkov gas field (Western Ukraine), 81

Caribbean oil, 132
Caroe, Sir Olaf, 161
Carpathian oil fields, see Western Ukraine
Carpathians, 8of.
Caspian Sea, 23, 24, 30, 71 (map), 75, 158
Catherine II, 7
Caucasus Mountains, 24, 25
Central Asiatic oil area, 99ff., 158
Central Ukraine, see Ukrainian SSR
Ceranti, see Chernovtsy
Chadysneft trust, 34, 73
Chakalov, 85, 90 (map)
Changelek oil field (Maykop area), 74
Changyrtash oil field (Fergana area), 100 (map), 102
Cheleken Island, 23, 76 (map), 77
Chelyabinsk, 52
Cherdyn gas field (Ukhta-Pechora area), 88 (map), 97, 99
Chernaya-Retchka oil field (Emba area), 95
Chernikovsk, 88 (map), 157
Chernomorneft trust, 34, 73
Chernovtsy (or Cernanti), 78 (map), 80, 81
Chimion oil field (Fergana area), 100 (map), 102
Chu oil field (Khirgiz area), 102
coal production, USSR, 56, 114
collectivization, 12
"Communist party of the Bolsheviki," 7, 157, 158
consumption, domestic, of oil, 54ff., 56 (table); by industry, 56; by transportation, 57; by agriculture, 58; by homes, 59; by armed forces, 59f.; in 1937, 60 (table)
conversion factors, 155
Cossacks, 6
Council of Ministers, 8
cracking, capacity, 53; lend-lease plants, 54n.
Crimea, 73, 79 (map)
czarist oil industry, 21ff.; lease system (1821-1872), 22; auction system (1872-1896), 22f.; combined auction and royalty system (1896-1917), 23; oil areas and oil production of, 23ff. (in Baku 23f.; foreign investments in, 28f.; 28 [table], processing and domestic demand, 29f., 30 [table]; transportation, 30f.; exports, 30ff.; Baku-Batumi pipeline, 30); exports of, 31 (table); domestic consumption and exports of, 32; end of, 32f.; nationalization of, 33

Czarna oil field (Western Ukraine), 81
Czechoslovakia, 135

Dagestan, 75
Dagneft trust, 35, 75
Dag Ogni gas field (Dagestan area), 71 (map), 75
Dashava gas field (Central Ukraine), 66, 78 (map), 81, 82
Decree of Land and Farming of 1917, 14
DeGolyer, E., 65
demand, see consumption
"democratic centralism," 8, 8n.
Derbent, 71 (map), 75
Dergachi gas field (Second Baku), 93 (map), 94
diesel oil, 54n.
Dnepropetrovsk, 72, 79 (map)
Dnieper River, 31, 77, 79 (map), 111-112n.
Doellen, W., 53n.
Dolina oil field (Western Ukraine), 78 (map), 81
Don River, 31, 79 (map), 111-112n.
Donets region, 70
Donets River, 77, 79 (map)
Dossor oil field (Emba area), 94, 95, 96 (map)
drilling, see production methods
drilling equipment, see production methods
Drogobych, 52, 78 (map), 81
Dshaksymai oil field (Emba area), 94, 95
Duff, Dahl M., 54n., 129n., 161
Duzlak gas field (Dagestan area), 75
Dzerzhinsk, 133
Dzhar-Kurgan oil field (Termez area), 100 (map), 102

Eastern Germany, 133, 135
eastern oil regions, 67, 85-105
Economist, the, 156
Egloff, Gustav, 53n., 65, 115n., 121n., 128
Ekhabil oil field (Sakhalin Island, 104 (map), 105
Emba oil region, 23, 24, 85, 94ff., 96 (map), 158
Emba River, 25, 96 (map)
Embaneft trust, 35, 95
Encumimsai oil field (Fergana area), 102
energy production, USSR, 111-112n., 114
energy supply, of world, 110 (table); of United States, 111 (table)
Engels, Friedrich, 10
Eno-Sing oil field (Fergana area), 102
Erdöl-Informationsdienst, 57, 158
Erdöl und Kohle, 42n., 54n., 65n., 82n., 110n., 115n., 118n., 121n., 130n., 134n.,

135n., 142n., 150n., 157, 158, 158n., 159, 159n., 160
Erivan, 9
Estonian SSR, 9, 66, 82, 83 (*map*), 84
Estonians, 6
Eternal Fire (Apsheron Peninsula), 21, 27n.
"Eurasian," 6
Europa Archiv, 7
Europe, oil and gas fields in, 36-37 (*map*); oil-handling ports in, 36-37 (*map*); pipelines in, 36-37 (*map*); refining centers in, 36-37 (*map*); sedimentary basins in, 36-37 (*map*)
exports of oil, 54, 55 (*table*), 60n.

Feigin, 161
Fergana, 52, 99, 100 (*map*), 102
Fergana Valley oil field (Fergana area), 23, 99, 100 (*map*), 102
Fischer, Louis, 33n.
Fischer-Tropsch process, 132
Five-Year Plans, 15ff.; first (1928-1932), 15, 41, 46, 56; second (1933-1937), 15, 41, 46, 49, 75; third (1938-1942), 15f., 41, 44, 46, 47, 49, 52, 77; fourth (1946-1950), 16 (production figures of, 16, 47, 49, 58, 66, 77, 81, 133, 158)
Fjodorov, S. F., 87n.
Focus, 130n., 161
Fohs, F. Julius, 161
forced labor, 99n.
Franz Josef Land, 3, 85, 98 (*map*)
Frunzl, 9, 102

Galician oil fields, *see* Western Ukraine
gasoline, 54n.
Gdov, 66, 82
"gusher," 89
gas-measurement method, *see* geophysics
Geological Committee, 38
Geological Museum, 39
geology, 38f.; Chief Administration for Geology and Geodesy, 38; Ministry of Geology, 39; prospecting, 39 (*table*); *see also* oil geology
geophysics, 35ff.; electrical method, 40, 41; gas-measurement method, 40f.; geophysical crews, 41 (*table*); gravitational method, 39f., 41; magnetic method, 40, 41; prospecting, 39ff.; seismic method, 40, 41
Georgian SSR, 9, 71 (*map*), 74f.
Georgians, 6
Giterman, Valentin, 6, 14n.
Glossary, 150
Golovatcheff, W., 112n.
Good, Dorothy, 37, 48, 161

Gorkig, 52, 133
Gorodki, 52, 87, 88 (*map*); refinery, 89
Gorski oil field (Groznyy area), 70
gravitational method, *see* geophysics
Graziorva oil field (Western Ukraine), 81
Great Russians, 6
Grigorjev, 58
Grozneft group, 34, 70
Groznyy, city, 24, 52, 69, 71 (*map*), 71f., 75
Groznyy oil region, 23, 24, 52, 70ff., 71 (*map*); production of, 72, 73 (*table*)
Grozneft trust, 35, 75
Gubkin, I. M., 65, 86, 89, 157, 158
Gudermes oil field (Groznyy area), 70, 71 (*map*)
Gunuski oil field (Groznyy area), 70
Gurylv, 52, 95, 96 (*map*), 97
"gusher," 157
Gyulbakht oil field (Baku area), 67, 68 (*map*)

Hartstock, Lydia, 42n.
heavy industry, 17f.
Hellin, P. F., 49n.
Hoetzsch, Otto, 6, 14n.
Holorveko oil field (Western Ukraine), 81
Hungary, 135, 135n.
Huxley, Julian, 35n.
hydrogenation, 132f., 159

Ilskiy oil field (Maykop area), 71 (*map*), 74
industrialization, 12
Institute for Geological Sciences, 39
Institute for Theoretical Geophysics, 39
Institute for Petroleum Geology, 39
Iran, 76 (*map*), 124 (*table*), 125, 141f.
Irkutsk, 52, 133
Ishimbay, 90 (*map*), 91, 157
Ishimbayneft trust, 24, 89
Ishimbay oil field (Second Baku), 86, 89, 90 (*map*), 157
Iskininskiy, 52, 95, 96 (*map*)
Iskininsky oil field (Emba area), 95, 96 (*map*), 97
Ivan IV, 7
Ivanovo, 85
Izberbash oil field (Dagestan area), 71 (*map*), 75
Ishimbay oil fields (Second Baku), 52, 89, 90 (*map*)
Izhevsk, 89, 90 (*map*), 99
Izhma gas field (Ukhta-Pechora area), 89, 98 (*map*), 99

Japan, actions on Sakhalin Island, 103
Jasienica oil field (Western Ukraine), 81

Journal of Soviet Science, 87n.
Jurin, M. N., 54n., 161

Kachreti, 75
Kaganovichneft trust, 34, 67
Kala oil field (Baku area), 68, 68 (*map*)
Kalininneft trust, 35, 102
Kaluga, 85
Kama oil fields (Second Baku), 89
Kama River, 87, 90 (*map*)
Kamishbashi oil field (Fergana area), 102
Kalamkarov, 54n.
Kaluyski oil field (Maykop area), 74
Kanibadam, 52
Kapeljushnikov, Russian engineer, 44
Kara Chukur oil field (Baku area), 68
Karadag oil field (Baku area), 67, 68 (*map*)
Karelo-Finnish SSR, 9
Katangli oil field (Sakhalin Island), 104 (*map*), 105
Kayakent oil field (Dagestan area), 71 (*map*), 75
Kazakh SSR (or Kazakhstan), 9, 16
Kazakhstanneft group, 35, 95
Kazan, 53
Kerch, 71 (*map*), 73
Kergez oil field (Baku area), 67, 68 (*map*)
Keslerovo-Varenikovo oil field (Maykop area), 74
Khabarovsk, 53, 105
Khadyzherskiy oil field (Maykop area), 71 (*map*), 74
Khanabad-Say oil field (Fergana area), 100 (*map*), 102
Kharkov, 77, 79 (*map*)
Khaudag oil field (Termez area), 100 (*map*), 102
Kherson, 53, 69, 79 (*map*)
Kiev, 9, 77, 78 (*map*), 82
Kim oil field (Fergana area), 100 (*map*), 102
Kinelneft trust, 34, 91
Kinel oil field (Second Baku), 91, 92 (*map*)
Kirghiz, 6
Kirghiz SSR, 9, 99, 101 (*map*)
Kirov, 85, 90 (*map*)
Kirovabad oil field (Termez area), 102
Kirovneft trust, 34, 67
Kishinev, 9
Klintshevsky, W., 6
Knorre, W. von, 22n., 31
Kokhtla-Yarve oil-shale deposits (Estonia), 82, 83 (*map*), 84
Komosol oil field (Kirghiz area), 102
Komsomolsk, 53, 105

Koschagyl oil field (Emba area), 95, 96 (*map*), 97
Kosmach oil field (Western Ukraine), 78 (*map*), 81
Kotlas, 98 (*map*), 99
Krasnodarneft group, 34, 73
Krasnodar, 53, 71 (*map*), 73, 74
Krasnokamneft trust, 34, 87
Krasnokamsk oil field (Second Baku), 87, 88 (*map*)
Krasnovodsk, 53, 69, 76 (*map*), 77
Krasnoyarsk, 53
Kropiwnik oil field (Western Ukraine), 81
Krymsky-Kudako oil field (Maykop area), 74
Kulmen oil field (Fergana area), 102
Kura Tsitse oil field (Maykop area), 74
Kurdyum gas field (Second Baku), 94
Kulsary oil field (Emba area), 95, 97
Kusiankul oil field (Second Baku), 89
Kusminovka oil field (Second Baku), 91
Kutais oil field (Maykop area), 71 (*map*), 74
Kuybyshev, 53, 54n., 85, 92 (*map*)
Kuybyshevneft group, 34, 91
Kuybyshev oil region (Second Baku), 91f., 92 (*map*)
Kyzyl-Tepe oil field (Baku area), 67

Lake Baykal, 48 (*map*), 132, 133, 159
Lake Peipus, 66, 82, 83 (*map*)
Latvian, SSR, 9
Latvians, 6
Lees, G. M., 128
Leeston, A. M., 86n., 95n., 127n., 161
Leimbach, Werner, 6, 34n., 35n., 57n., 58n., 95, 95n., 116n., 117n.
Lemberg, Eugen, 6, 14n., 16n.
Lena River basin, 158n.
Lenczorvsky, George, 161
lend-lease, 54n.
Lenin, V. I., 7, 8, 8n., 14, 15, 45
Lenin oil fields, 67
Leningrad, 53, 84
Leninneft trust, 34, 67
Leninsk, 53, 100 (*map*), 102
"Lenin-Stalinism," 7
Leuna, 133
Lianosov, G. M., oil companies, 27, 33
Lipiz oil field (Western Ukraine), 81
Lithuanian SSR, 9
Lithuanians, 6
Lok-Batan oil field (Baku area), 67
Lodyna oil field (Western Ukraine), 81
Lomna oil field (Western Ukraine), 81
London Tribune, 142
Lvov, 53, 78 (*map*), 81, 82

INDEX

magnetic method, *see* geophysics

Magnitogorsk, 89, 90 (*map*)

Mahomedly oil field, 67, 68 (*map*)

Main-Post (Würzburg), 49n.

Majdan oil field (Western Ukraine), 81

Makat oil field (Emba area), 94, 95, 96 (*map*), 97

Makhachkala, 53, 69, 70, 71 (*map*), 72, 75

Makhety oil field (Groznyy area), 70

Malgobekneft trust, 34, 70

Malgobek oil field (Groznyy area), 70, 71 (*map*), 72, 73

Malisay oil field (Fergana area), 102

Malzahn, E., 161

Mamangan oil field (Fergana area), 102

Mangshlak oil field (Turkmen area), 77

Mannesmann tubes, 131

Mantashev, A. I., oil companies, 27, 33

Markorva oil field (Western Ukraine), 81

Marvin, Charles, 27n.

Marx, Karl, 10ff.

Matzen oil field (Austria), 136

Maykop oil region, 23, 24, 52, 71 (*map*), 72, 73f.; production in, 74 (*table*)

Mazut oil trading company, 27

Meissner, Boris, 7

Melnikovo oil field (Fergana area), 102

Melnikovo, 53, 102

Mexico, 124 (*table*), 125

Miadzhik gas field (Baku area), 67, 68 (*map*), 69

Middle East, 141ff.

Minsk, 9

Michailov, N., 6

Mining Journal, 49n.

Mironov, S. J., 87n.

Mirzaani, 53

Moldavian SSR, 9

Molotov (formerly Perm), 53, 85, 88 (*map*); oil region, 87ff.; refinery in, 89; gas pipeline through, 99

Molotovneft group, 34

Molotovneft trust, 34, 67, 87

Monde, Le, 141n.

Moniteur du Pétrole Roumain, 56n.

Moscow, 9, 53, 92, 99

Moskalvo, 53, 104 (*map*), 105

Mraznica oil field (Western Ukraine), 81

Nadvornaya, 53, 81

Nahujorvice oil field (Western Ukraine), 81

Naphtha Production Company Nobel Brothers oil company, 26; nationalization of, 26; capital of, 27

natural gas, 159; consumption in 1950 of, 66n.; in Dashava field, 78 (*map*), 82, 89;

deposits of, 66; in Fergana area, 99, 102; pipelines, 72, 75, 91, 92; production of, in Baku area, 69; production of, in Saratov area, 92f.; reserves of, 66; in Ukhta-Pechora, 97; in Western Ukraine, 81

Nebit-Dag, 53, 76 (*map*), 77

Neft oil company, 27

Nefteabad oil field (Fergana area), 100 (*map*), 102

Neftechala oil field (Baku area), 68

Neftedag oil field (Turkmen area), 77

Nettleton, L. L., 39n.

Neue Welt, 58n.

Neue Züricher Zeitung, 131n.

New Economic Policy (NEP), 14f., 45

New Groznyy oil field, 24, 70ff.

New York Times, 8, 18n., 95n., 159n.

Nikolayev, 53, 69, 79 (*map*)

Nikolajevsk, 53, 104 (*map*), 105

Nineteenth Congress of the Communist Party, 158

Nobel concern, 26ff., 33

Nobel, Ludwig, 26

Nobel, Robert, 26

Nordvik, 48 (*map*), 158, 159

Norins, Martin R., 161

Norio oil field (Georgia), 75

North Pole, 3

Novobogatinskoye, 53, 95, 96 (*map*)

Novobogatinskoye oil field (Emba area), 95, 96 (*map*)

Nutovo oil field (Sakhalin Island), 105

October Revolution of 1917, 7, 14, 77

Odessa, 53, 69, 78 (*map*), 135

offshore drilling, *see* underwater drilling

Ohio State University, 55n.

Oil and Gas Journal, 54n., 65n., 123, 123n., 129n., 133n., 135n., 141n., 149

oil companies, 26ff.; investments in czarist era of, 26f.; production of, 1910-1914, 27 (*table*)

oil demand of the Soviet Union, 109ff., factors determining, 115ff. (size of territory, 116; agriculture, 116f.; army, 116f.; population, 117; urbanization, 117f.; technology, 119f.; political element, 119); potential curtailment of, 119ff.; satisfaction of, 121ff.; imports to cover, 133f.

oil geology, 35ff., 36-37 (*map*), 68, 69, 70, 74, 75, 77, 86n., 12, 89, 91, 95, 157; exploration, 38, 157f.; Institute for Petroleum Geology, 39, 157

oil groups, *see* Soviet oil industry

oil industry in planned economy and free enterprise system, 123ff., 124 (*table*)

[169]

oil production (world, U.S.A., and USSR), 112 (*table*), 113 (*chart*)

oil products, *see* products

oil refining, *see* refining

oil shale, deposits of, 66, 159n.; in Estonia, 82ff., 83 (*map*), 84 (*table*); reserves of, 66

oil supply of Soviet Union, 109; compared with demand, 120; synthetic oil production and, 131f.; imports, 133f.

oil trusts, *see* Soviet oil industry

oil wells, number of, 51, 130

Okha, 53, 104 (*map*), 105

Okha oil field (Sakhalin Island), 104 (*map*), 105

Oktyabrneft trust, 34, 70

Oktyabrskiy, 89, 90 (*map*), 157

Old Groznyy oil field, 24, 70ff.

Öl und Kohle, p. 53n.

Opaka oil field (Western Ukraine), 81

Ordzonikidzeneft trust, 34, 67; deep drilling in, 42

Orow oil field (Western Ukraine), 81

Orsk, 53, 54n., 94, 95, 96 (*map*), 97

Osipenko, 53

Otto, Nikolaus, and "Otto Gas Machine," 30n.

Overiata oil field (Second Baku), 89

Palvan-Tash oil and gas field (Fergana area), 100 (*map*), 102

paraffin, in Second Baku crude oil, 159

Parket oil field (Fergana area), 102

Pasieczna gas field (Western Ukraine), 81

Pechora railroad, 98 (*map*), 99

Pechora River, 97, 98 (*map*)

Peking, 136

Penza, 85, 92 (*map*)

per-capita production of USSR and other countries in 1951, 156 (*table*)

Pereginsko oil field (Western Ukraine), 78 (*map*), 81

personnel, trained, and Soviet oil industry, 129, 129n.

Peschany Island oil field (Baku area), 68

Peter I, 7, 97

"Petersburg age" (1689-1917), 7

Petroleum, 22n.

Petroleum Engineer, 53n., 115n.

Petroleum Press Service, 44n., 54n., 58n., 65n., 66n., 86n., 111-112n., 115n., 118n., 119n., 121n., 158n., 159n.

Petroleum Times, 86n.

Petrozavodsk, 9

Pier, Matthias, 132

Pierce, A., 42n.

pig iron production, 56

pipelines, first, 26; connecting Ural-Volga region and industrial areas, 46; from Baku, 68; to Batumi, 68; in Groznyy area, 72; in Maykop area, 74; in Georgia, 75; in Dagestan, 75; in Turkmen area, 77; in Estonia, 84; in Molotov area, 89; in Ufa region, 91; in Kuybyshev region, 91f.; from Sarasov to Moscow for gas, 92f.; in Western Ukraine, 81, 94n.; in Emba region, 95, 97; in Ukhta-Pechora area, 99; in Central Asiatic area, 102; on Sakhalin Island, 105; *see also* natural gas

Pirsagat oil field (Baku area), 68

Pitaussay oil field (Fergana area), 102

planned economy, 12ff., 15ff., 46

Ploesti, 135

Ploskie oil field (Western Ukraine), 81

Poelitz, 133, 159

Polana oil field (Western Ukraine), 81

Poland, 78 (*map*), 80, 81, 82n.

Polazna oil field (Second Baku), 89

Poltava oil field (Central Ukraine), 77, 79 (*map*)

Porohy oil field (Western Ukraine), 81

Poronay oil field (Sakhalin Island), 105

Pratt, Wallace E., 37, 48, 161

Pravda, 118n.

Pravoberezhnoye gas field (Groznyy area), 70

products, aviation gasoline, 59, 159; diesel motor oil, 58; fuel oil, 57, 58; glossary of, 150; kerosene, 59, 59n., 159; "light products," 159; lubricants, 56, 58

production methods, 42ff.; deep drilling, 42f.; drilling, 42ff.; drilling equipment, 159; drilling performance, 44 (*table*); electro drilling, 157; production of oil by mining, 97; rotary drilling, 42; turbine drilling, 44, 157; *see also* underwater drilling

Przemysl, 80, 81

Puta oil field (Baru area), 67, 68 (*map*)

railroad system, 57

Rakusha, 97

refining and refineries, capacity of, 51f., 53, 53n., 54n; location of, 52f.; output of, 52f., 157, 159; in Baku, 68; in Dagestan, 75; in Emba region, 95; in Fergana, 102; in Georgia, 75; in Groznyy, 70f.; in Gorodki, 89; in Kuybyshev, 91; in Nebit-Dag, 77; in Maykop, 74; in Molotov, 89

reserves, 65, 158; classification of, 65, 150f.; problems of, 127ff.

Reval, *see* Tallin

Ristananto oil field (Fergana area), 102

INDEX

Romany (Lenin) oil field (Baku area), 23, 67, 68 (map)

Romny oil field (Central Ukraine), 77, 79 (map)

Rosochy oil field (Western Ukraine), 81

Rostov, 69, 71 (map), 72

Rosu, George G., 133n., 161

rotary drilling, see production methods

Roth, Andrew, 142

Rothschilds, bankers, 27, 28

Royal Dutch-Shell group, 26ff., 29, 33

Rumania, 134f., 134 (table)

Russian crude-oil production, 1861-1950, compared with that of world and U.S., 147f.

Russian General Oil Corporation (RGOC), 26ff., 33

Russian oil production, 25; 1908-1916, 25 (table)

Russian Soviet Federated Socialist Republic (RSFSR), 9, 70, 73, 75

Russo-Chinese Treaty of 1950, 136

Russo-Japanese War of 1905, 103

Ryizan, 85

Rypne gas field (Western Ukraine), 91

Sabsa Ompareti oil field (Georgia), 75

Sabunchi oil field (Baku area), 23, 67, 68 (map)

Sagiz oil field (Emba area), 95, 96 (map)

Sakhalin Island, 23, 35, 103, 103 (table), 104 (map), 105, 133, 158

Sakhalinneft trust, 35, 105

salt plugs in Emba area, 95

Saratov, 53, 66, 82, 85, 92 (map), 93 (map); gas field at, 86

Saryncha oil field (Baku area), 67

Schwartz, Harry, 18, 161

Sea of Azov, 69, 71 (map)

secondary recovery, see production methods

Second Baku, 84-86, 88 (map), 90 (map), 92 (map), 93 (map); production in, 86 (table); development of, 157; and passim

seismic method, see geophysics

Sepsil oil field (Maykop area), 74

Sevastopol, 69

Seventeenth Congress of the Communist Party, 157

Seventeenth International Geological Congress, v

Severokamneft trust, 34, 87

Severokamsk oil field (Second Baku), 87, 89

Shabad, Theodore, 4, 5, 68, 71, 76, 79, 83, 88, 90, 92, 93, 96, 98, 100, 101, 103n., 104, 113, 161

shale oil, 84, 84 (table), 154

Shibajeff oil company, 27

Shilovo oil field (Second Baku), 89

Shimkin, D. B., 43n., 45n., 47n., 51n., 52n., 53n., 54n., 57n., 58n., 59n., 60n., 66n., 149, 159, 161, 162

Shiraki oil field (Maykop area), 74

Shiraki oil field (Georgia), 74

Shomgar oil field (Baku area), 67

Shorsu oil field (Fergana area), 100 (map), 102

Shubany oil field (Baku area), 67, 68 (map)

Shubar-Kuduk oil field (Emba area), 94, 95, 96 (map)

Shuraabad oil field (Baku area), 68

Siam Shor oil field (Baku area), 68

Siazan oil field (Baku area), 68

Siberia, 16, 48 (map), 158, 159

Siegrist, Marie, 162

Sieget, Alexander, 35n.

"silk road," 136n.

Sinkiang, 136

Skhodnitsa-Urycez oil field (Western Ukraine), 81

slave labor, 99n.

Slobodo-Nybielowska oil field (Western Ukraine), 91

Smakaevo oil field (Second Baku), 89

Smirnov, L. P., 157, 157n., 162

Smith, Walter Bedell, vi, 142

socialization, 12

Société Caspienne et de la Mer Noire, 27, 28

Solna oil field (Western Ukraine), 81

southwestern oil regions, 67ff.

Soviet armed forces, consumption of oil by, 59f., 116f., 122

Soviet council system, 8

Soviet economic theory, 10f.

Sredasneft group, 35

Stalin, Joseph, 7, 8, 13, 14n., 16, 119, 131

Stalinabad, 9

Stalinneft trust, 34, 67

Stalingrad, 53

Stalino, 72, 79 (map)

Standard Oil (N.J.), 27, 33

Staragrozneft trust, 34, 70

Starunia oil field (Western Ukraine), 81

Stavropolneft trust, 34, 91

Stavropol, 91, 92 (map)

Stebinger, Eugene, 160

steel supply of Soviet oil industry, 131; compared with that of U.S. oil industry, 129f., 130 (table)

Sterlitamak, 53, 90 (map), 157

Stryy, 53, 78 (*map*), 81
Strzelbice, 53, 81
Strzelbice oil field (Western Ukraine), 81
Sultangulovo gas field (Second Baku), 90
  (*map*), 91, 92 (*map*)
Sulu Tepe oil field (Baku area), 68
Supreme Soviet of the Soviet Union, 8
Surakhany oil field (Baku area), 23, 67,
  68, 68 (*map*)
Suvorov-Cherkess oil field (Maykop area),
  74
Sverdlovsk, 87, 90 (*map*)
synthetic-oil production, 131f.; goal for,
  133; actual, 133
Syzranneft trust, 34, 91
Syzran oil fields (Second Baku), 53, 86,
  89, 91f., 92 (*map*)

Tadzhik SSR, 9, 99, 101 (*map*)
Tadzhiks, 6
Tallin, 9, 83 (*map*), 84
Taman Peninsula, 71 (*map*), 73, 74
tankers, 26; Russian and world totals of,
  57n.; *see also* Zoroaster
Tashkalaneft trust, 34, 70
Tashkent, 9
Tatar Autonomous SSR, 90 (*map*), 92
  (*map*), 158
Tartars, 6
Tbilisi (or Tiflis), 9, 53, 75
Teplovka gas field (Second Baku), 94
Termen-yelga oil field (Second Baku), 91
Termez oil district (Fergana area), 101
  (*map*), 102
Thiel, Erich, 57n., 114n.
Thompson, O. B., 162
Tien Shan Mountains, 136n.
Tolpin, J. G., 86n.
tractors, use of, 58, 121, 121n.; oil con-
  sumption of, 58, 59
Trans-Caucasian Railroad, 31
transportation, development of, 57f., 130,
  130n., 159; *see also* pipelines
Trudovaya, 72
Tuapse, 53, 71 (*map*), 72, 73, 74
Tula, 85
turbine drilling, 44
Turkic ethnic group, 6
Turkmen Canal, 112n.
Turkmen, ethnic group, 6
Turkmenneft trust, 35, 76
Turkmen SSR, 9, 69, 76 (*map*), 101 (*map*);
  oil district, 75f.; production in, 77
Tuymazy, 53, 90 (*map*), 92 (*map*), 157
Tuymazyneft trust, 34, 89
Tuymazy oil fields (Second Baku), 86, 89,
  90 (*map*), 92 (*map*), 157

Uch-Kyzyl oil field (Termez area), 102
Ufa, 53, 54n., 85, 90 (*map*), 91, 157
Ufa oil region (Second Baku), 89f., 90
  (*map*)
Ukhta, 53, 97, 99
Ukhta-Pechora oil region, 35, 85, 97ff., 98
  (*map*), 158
Ukhta River, 97, 98 (*map*)
Ukrainian SSR, 9, 78-79 (*map*), Central
  Ukraine, 77f., 79 (*map*); Western Ukraine
  (Carpathian) oil fields, 66, 78 (*map*),
  80f.; production in, 80 (*table*), 81 (*table*)
Ukrainians, 6
Ukrneft trust, 35, 77, 81
underwater drilling, 43, 43n., 158
Union of Soviet Socialist Republics
  (USSR), arable soil in, 5; area of, 3; forest area of, 5; population of, 6; vegetation zones of, 4 (*map*), 5 (*map*); birth
  rate of, 6; history of, 6f.; constitution
  of, 7, 9; political organization of, 8f.;
  constituent republics of, 9; economy of,
  9ff.; economic provisions of constitution
  of, 12f.; industrial areas of, their geographical location, centers, and mineral
  deposits, 17f.; products and production
  figures of, p. 18; *and passim*
Ural River, 25, 90 (*map*), 95, 96 (*map*)
Urals, 65, 85, 90 (*map*), 97; central part
  of, 88 (*map*)
urbanization, 117f., 118 (*table*)
Uzbek ethnic group, 6
Uzbek SSR, 9, 99, 101 (*map*)

Vasyutin, 160
Velikovsky, A. S., 162
Venezuela, 124, 124 (*table*)
Verkhne-Chusooskiye Gorodki oil field
  (Second Baku), 86, 87, 88 (*map*)
Vigrek oil field (Sakhalin Island), 105
Vilna, 9
Vipper, R. J., 7
Vladivostok, 53, 105
Volga-Moscow Canal (Moscow Canal), 86
Volga River, 31, 66, 85, 92 (*map*), 93
  (*map*), 111-112n.
Volkswirt, Der, 50n.
Voroshilovneft trust, 35, 102
Vosnessenka oil field (Groznyy area), 70
Vosnessenskij, N. A., 16n.

Wartanoff, Boris, 162
waterways, 57
Wax Mountain oil field (Maykop area), 74
Weber, Adolf, 9, 10n., 14n., 16n., 35n., 55n.
Welt, Die, 112n.
Western Ukraine, *see* Ukrainian SSR

INDEX

White Russians, 6

Witwica oil field (Western Ukraine), 81

Wolica-Kroscienko oil field (Western Ukraine), 81

Wolosianka-Mala oil field (Western Ukraine), 81

world crude-oil production, 1948-1950, 149f.

World Oil, 54n., 65n., 130n., 148

world oil production, 155f. *(table)*

Wusu oil fields (Sinkiang), 136n.

Wyoming, U.S.A., 42

World War II, 47, 54n.

Wszelaki, Jan, 162

Yablonovo oil field (Second Baku), 91

Yakutsk, 158n.

Yarega River, 97, 98 *(map)*

Yaroslavl, 53

Yelshanka (Saratov) natural-gas field (Second Baku), 94

Zhdanov, 69, 79 *(map)*

Ziestersdorf oil field (Austria), 136

Zimmermann, Erich W., 111n.

Zischka, Anton, 50n., 136n.

Zoroaster, first tanker, 26

Zykh oil field (Baku area), 68, 68 *(map)*